Experiments in General Chemistry

THIRD EDITION

Heiko Jacobsen

Tulane University

FOUNTAINHEAD
PRESS

Our "green" initiatives include:

Electronic Products
We deliver products in non-paper form whenever possible. This includes pdf downloadables, flash drives, & CDs.

Electronic Samples
We use Xample, a new electronic sampling system. Instructor samples are sent via a personalized web page that links to pdf downloads.

FSC Certified Printers
All of our printers are certified by the Forest Service Council which promotes environmentally and socially responsible management of the world's forests. This program allows consumer groups, individual consumers, and businesses to work together hand-in-hand to promote responsible use of the world's forests as a renewable and sustainable resource.

Recycled Paper
Most of our products are printed on a minimum of 30% post-consumer waste recycled paper.
Support of Green Causes
When we do print, we donate a portion of our revenue to green causes. Listed below are a few of the organizations that have received donations from Fountainhead Press. We welcome your feedback and suggestions for contributions, as we are always searching for worthy initiatives.

Rainforest 2 Reef
Environmental Working Group

Cover design by Doris Bruey
Text design by Patricia Bracken
Figures © 2010, Heiko Jacobsen
Figures C-1, 1-2 © Fountainhead Press
Figure 10-2 (reproduced from Wikipedia)

Books may be purchased for educational purposes.

For information, please call or write:

1-800-586-0330

Fountainhead Press
Southlake, TX 76092

Web site: www.fountainheadpress.com
Email: customerservice@fountainheadpress.com

ISBN 978-1-59871-061-8
Third Edition
Printed in the United States of America

TABLE OF CONTENTS

ISAGOGE

The laboratory manual "Experiments in General Chemistry" summarizes the course activities for the class sequence CHEM117 (General Chemistry Lab I) and CHEM118 (General Chemistry Lab II) as currently taught at Tulane University. The experiments complement the lectures in General Chemistry; they explore basic concepts of chemistry, such as chemical reactions, thermochemistry and thermodynamics, chemical kinetics and chemical equilibrium, as well as colligative properties and electrochemistry.

The current format of the manual also reflects the developments of this course during the post-Katrina period in New Orleans; a time that is characterized by recovery, rebuilding, redefining, and restructuring. The lab manual is a work in progress, and the efforts to improve and refine the main body of this work are ongoing.

A large number of individuals have contributed to the development of this laboratory manual; space does not permit a comprehensive list of all the parties involved. I acknowledge the work of previous instructors who laid the cornerstones for some of the very basic experiments. I am especially thankful to the many teaching assistants, who over the last years have diligently worked in the General Chemistry laboratory, and who to a main part are responsible for the success of the classes CHEM117 and CHEM118.

Heiko Jacobsen

New Orleans, May 2008

TOOLS OF THE TRADE

I have always wanted to know as much as possible about the world.

—LINUS PAULING

A — Laboratory Notebook

Learning to keep a laboratory notebook is one of the most important skills a scientist needs to master. The notebook is the commonly recognized tool used by scientists to store information necessary to enable experiments to be repeated in the future, whether by the scientist herself or himself, or by someone else. The notebook, therefore, should be kept in a neat and organized fashion since it may be used by others, perhaps dozens of years after the time it was originally written. Keeping a laboratory notebook is standard procedure in every lab where new chemicals and new chemical procedures are invented and eventually have to be patented. To chemists and biochemists, the lab notebook is the most precious document in their labs, because it documents their procedures. It is a legally valid record that preserves your rights or those of an employer or academic investigator to your discoveries. It also allows you to backtrack and to repeat a procedure, and it allows you to catch and document possible errors.

The advantage of sound record keeping is that it allows you to defend your data at a later date if necessary, and that someone else, be it your teaching assistant, lab instructor or your supervisor, can easily locate pertinent data and results in your notebook. Although reasonable legibility and neatness are highly desirable, the usefulness of a notebook is largely determined by it being *permanent*, *original*, *systematic*, and *complete*, not perfect. Thus, the laboratory notebook should be a tool used in the laboratory while collecting the data. Entire books have been written on how to properly write and maintain a laboratory notebook. *Writing the Laboratory Notebook*, by Howard M. Kanare, American Chemical Society (1985), is one example of a good guide book.

A.1 Format of a notebook

While there is no standard format used by all scientists, the following is a summary of the key elements that are to be included in a laboratory notebook.

1) The notebook is to be bound with numbered pages. Your notebook should have double pages for making carbon copies of your report that might be turned in to your teaching assistant, lab instructor, or supervisor.

2) Entries are to be made in permanent ink; do not use pencil. Notes in pencil are not permanent and their presence may arouse doubt about the integrity of the worker. If a mistake is made, cross it out with a single horizontal line. Do *not* tear out the page or block out the written material containing a mistake; you may still want to refer to it later. If data entries are being corrected, give a reason for the correction. Simply write a short note following the invalid data explaining why it it should be overlooked.

3) Notebook pages are to be used consecutively. Avoid skipping pages, even if another experiment is started before a previous one is completed. Entries may be double-spaced if this will make the notebook more legible, and space may be allocated in tables for convenient data entry.

4) Begin with a fresh page for each new lab experiment. Do not crowd your lab notebook since most notebooks have more than ample room for the semester's lab experiments.

5) Procedures and other information should never be copied from another author. They should be summarized in your own words with reference made to the original work (if applicable). If work is performed with the aid of a partner or a teaching assistant, credit for that person's contribution should also be noted.

6) All data should be recorded promptly and *directly* in your lab notebook as you are doing the experiment. *Never* write data on loose paper, in another notebook, in the laboratory manual, on paper towels, etc., with the idea of copying it into your lab notebook at a later time. While neatness may be somewhat sacrificed by recording data directly, preventing loss of data and eliminating transcribing errors more than counterbalance this factor.

7) The record must include poor results as well as successful ones. Faulty experiments should be so labeled and you should include possible reasons for their failure. A laboratory notebook — in a research lab, a government lab, an industrial lab — is a legal record and should be regarded as such.

8) Before leaving the laboratory, look over your notes and add any additional observations or labels that you may have omitted earlier.

A.2 Format of a lab report

A good lab report does more than present data; it demonstrates the writer's comprehension of the concepts behind the data. Merely recording the expected and observed results is not sufficient. You should also identify how and why differences occurred, explain how they affected your experiment, and show your understanding of the principles the experiment was designed to examine. Bear in mind that a format, however helpful, cannot replace clear thinking and organized writing. You still need to organize your ideas carefully and express them coherently.

There exist many formats of writing a lab report. Regardless of variations, however, the goal of lab reports remains the same: *document* your findings and *communicate* their significance. Described below is one particular format that might be used to create lab reports for the experiments described in this manual.

A.2.1 Heading: Names of people responsible for the experiment (e.g. names of experimenters, instructors, room and/or section numbers, if applicable), the experiment number and title, the date the experiment was or will be performed, and partner's name(s), if applicable.

A.2.2 Objective or Purpose: A one or two-sentence statement of what one hopes to accomplish by performing the experiment.

A.2.3 Apparatus: A list of the equipment needed, including specific information such as type, size, or model number.

A.2.4 Reagents: An itemization of the chemicals to be used and the amount required of each. Be specific about the exact form of each reagent (e.g. pure solid; aqueous solution, including concentration; and so on). Also include any notes on special hazards or precautions associated with particular reagents (e.g. corrosive, flammable, avoid contact with skin).

A.2.5 Plan of Procedure or Graphical Abstract: If your intention is to perform a new experiment, or to establish new experimental procedures, it is of paramount importance that you present a detailed *plan of procedure*. On the other hand, if you set out to verify or repeat an established experiment, a mere repetition of an already published procedure is not very helpful, and you will want to create a *graphical abstract*. Draw a concise picture illustrating one of the core concepts of the experiment to be performed. To do so, read the instructions carefully, identify the gist of the experiment, pinpoint key aspects of the theory behind the procedure, and establish the crux of the experimental methodology. Transform the words into a drawing, and support your figure with a short caption. Depending on your assessment of the experiment, you might want to create an all-encompassing pictorial rendition, or you might want to focus on one particular aspect that you consider key. This exercise allows you to form a visual image of the experimental procedure. As a result, you will be better prepared for doing the lab experiment and will be able to complete the work faster. This exercise further allows an independent reader to put the work presented into a broader and more meaningful perspective.

A.2.6 Additional pre-lab components: Some additional pre-lab requirements are helpful to clarify particular aspects of the experiment. These pre-lab components might include references to literature work, or might address concepts and theoretical aspects in more detail. For experiments performed as part of a laboratory course, the pre-lab components are often based on a set of pre-lab questions. This, however, does not mean that pre-lab questions should be treated like a test or a quiz. Do not simply present unsupported answers that, when read without knowledge of the underlying question, are rather meaningless (e.g. "1. 0.3 mL" or "2d. double displacement"). Instead, formulate an explanatory statement that not only incorporates answers to the pre-lab questions, but also elucidates particular aspects of the experiment, be it of a fundamental or a technical nature.

A.2.7 Data and Observations: Record the observations and measurements made while carrying out the procedure. Include any changes you made to the procedure as originally laid out and any mistakes that were made. Observe carefully and report what happened in the experiment (e.g. colors of solutions and indicators, smells and other subjective evaluations). These observations may help you make decisions as to the statistical significance of your experimental results as well as to possible reasons for its success or failure. Be sure to reference for which trial(s) the observation was valid, and which trial(s) deviated from the expected observation. In recording data, take care to record the results of measurements (e.g. masses, volumes, temperatures) to the exact number of significant figures given by the measuring device. You should tabulate data when appropriate and include all units of measure. Recording data in a table helps to keep your notebook neat and legible. *You will be able to save valuable laboratory time by thinking ahead and setting up these tables before coming to the laboratory.*

A.2.8 Calculations and Results: An organized summary of data recorded while performing the experiment and any data reduction, calculations, and error analysis made using that data. Calculations and interpretation of data can be done outside the laboratory. All calculations should be recorded in the notebook. Give sample formulas for the calculation procedure. Confirm to the rules for significant figures and data reduction. The use of tables is encouraged in dealing with the organization of calculation results. Each individual experiment may contain additional guidelines for calculations and results. It is not necessary to explicitly perform standardized computational procedures, such as calculation of average and standard deviation. Use the functions of pocket calculators and spread sheets to obtain the desired result. If you do so, reference the calculator or program you have used to achieve your results in your lab report.

A.2.9 *Discussion and Conclusions:* A summary and interpretation of results. If you have carried out a new experiment, the discussion should always include, *but should not be limited to*, the answers to these questions:

 i. What has been learned from this experiment?

 ii. What changes, if any, could be made to improve this experiment?

 iii. What are the most significant sources of error in this experiment? *Be specific* and discuss how the error source can affect the results.

 If you have repeated an already established experiment, the discussion should always include, *but should not be limited to*, the answers to these questions:

 i. Are the expectations based on the graphical abstract justified?

 ii. What is the most important aspect of the experiment?

 iii. Which aspects of the experiment, if any, could be improved?

A.2.10 *Signature and Date:* Your signature at the end of the day's work.

B — Laboratory Safety

The chemistry laboratory can be a dangerous place. For instance, Bunsen burner flames can exceed 1000°C and certain materials can cause severe health issues with ingestion of amounts less than what can fit on the head of a pin. Fortunately, federal regulations have been implemented to protect us while we work in the lab. In accordance with these regulations, we must follow certain safety guidelines while we are in the laboratory. Keep in mind that it is often not your own work, but the activities of other people working in the lab that puts you in potentially dangerous situations. Even if you have finished all your experiments and are just completing your lab notebook entries, always keep wearing at least your eye protection.

B.1 Rules of Safety

The following list is not a complete itemization of all aspects of safety that have to be followed in a chemistry lab. The points addressed however are applicable to all experiments that are described in this lab manual.

B.1.1 *Eye protection must be worn at all times in the laboratory.* Many laboratory chemicals and techniques present health hazards, but the eyes are particularly vulnerable to chemical injury. Carelessness leads to accidents that can cause severe eye injury and even blindness. Always wear at least safety glasses, even if you are not performing experiments with chemicals. Safety glasses protect you injuries due to glass damage or similar occurrences. If you use particularly dangerous chemicals such as concentrated acids, wear safety goggles instead of just safety glasses. If a chemical splashes onto your face, do not remove your goggles. First rinse your face thoroughly, and then remove your goggles and flush out your eyes at the eye wash station for a minimum of ten minutes.

B.1.2 Do not wear contact lenses. Chemicals can get underneath the contact lenses and cause severe damage to the eyes. Some contact lenses can absorb chemical vapors. This can be a problem particularly with soft contact lenses. Should an accident occur, flushing your eye with the contact lenses in place will prevent the removal of the chemical from underneath the lens. In extreme cases contact lenses can become fused to the eye, requiring surgical removal.

B.1.3 Wear sensible clothes to lab that cover your body. When working in the lab, wear long pants and closed-toe shoes. Sandals, open toe shoes, shorts and skirts that do not extend to the knees, halter tops, and shirts that expose the abdomen or back are not allowed in the lab. You should not wear items of clothing that have puffy sleeves and redundant fabric; these can easily catch on fire. If you prefer not to bother about what attire you wear in the lab, purchase and wear a lab coat, which will provide suitable protection. Long hair (shoulder length or longer) must be put in a ponytail or controlled in some fashion; hair will burn very quickly if ignited. Wear gloves for handling corrosive chemicals and solvents and washing glassware.

B.1.4 Know the location of all safety equipment in your particular laboratory and how each item is used. This equipment includes the eye wash stations, fire extinguishers, fire blankets, fire alarm, safety showers, and emergency exits. In the event of an accident, always shout for assistance first. Be sure to notify the lab instructor and the laboratory director of any injury or accident, no matter how small it seems.

B.1.5 Read the labels on bottles carefully. The wrong choice of chemical could ruin your experiment and could also cause a hazardous reaction. Do not take reagent bottles to your lab bench since these are for the use of the entire class. Take approximately what you need with a clean spatula or piece of glassware that is clean and dry. Do not waste chemicals by taking more than is required and never return unused chemicals to their bottles. Dispose of them appropriately.

B.1.6 Dispose of waste properly. Check for special bottles labeled for waste before disposing of anything. Do not use the sink for solid or liquid disposal unless your laboratory instructor has told you it is permissible. Solid materials will generally be disposed of in waste containers. For all disposal questions, ask your laboratory instructor for guidance. Broken glass must be disposed of in special waste containers. Do not put broken glass in trash cans or sinks. Do not put paper in the broken glass barrels. Improper disposal of glass is a major cause of injury to the physical plant personnel and others.

B.1.7 Take care of spills immediately. Some chemicals are toxic and must be removed carefully with the aid of appropriate methods. One such example is the clean up of mercury from a broken thermometer. Other spills are less problematic. However, all spills should be dealt with immediately to prevent injury to people and damage to equipment. ALL spills are to be reported to the laboratory instructor for clear instructions on cleanup.

B.1.8 Avoid pointing a test tube at yourself or anyone else when you are heating it. The proper way to heat a test tube is to point it away from everyone. Holding it at an angle to the bench top, move it back and forth in the hottest part of the Bunsen burner flame. Do not point the test tube toward anyone even after it has been removed from the flame. The contents can still bump out until it has cooled.

B.1.9 Dilute concentrated acids by adding the acid to the water. This is especially important for concentrated sulfuric and phosphoric acids, which can generate enough heat when diluted with water to cause the solution to boil.

B.1.10 Prepare for each experiment by reading the assigned laboratory procedure before arriving. Follow directions carefully and precisely as instructed in the manual, unless your instructor directs you otherwise. Your laboratory instructor is there to answer questions and to help with any problems. Do not work alone in the laboratory. Enter the laboratory only if a laboratory instructor or a substitute is allows you to.

B.1.11 Food and drink are not allowed in the laboratory. You can contaminate container even if unopened with absorption from the air in the lab. This can cause illness and more severe effects of poisoning in some cases. Do not use tobacco in any form, including "mint snuff', or chew gum in the lab. These constitute easy ways of ingesting poisons. Smoking is also an easy way of starting a fire when working with organic chemicals.

B.1.12 Keep the lab clean at all times. This can prevent many accidents. It is easy to knock things over in a cluttered environment. It also is easy to put your hand, your notebook, or some other valuable object into a spill that has not been cleaned up. Keep your books, purses, coats, etc. off the lab bench. They can be damaged or even cause an accident. Place them out of your work area. Clean balances after you use them. Any spills you leave behind could cause an accident. Always clean your work area and wash your hands before leaving.

C — Laboratory Equipment

Laboratory equipment is generally used to either perform an experiment or to take measurements and gather data. Chemists use special tools such as Bunsen burners, or glassware such as an Erlenmeyer flask. Items commonly used in the chemistry laboratory are shown in Figure C-1.

Figure C-1: Items commonly used in the laboratory

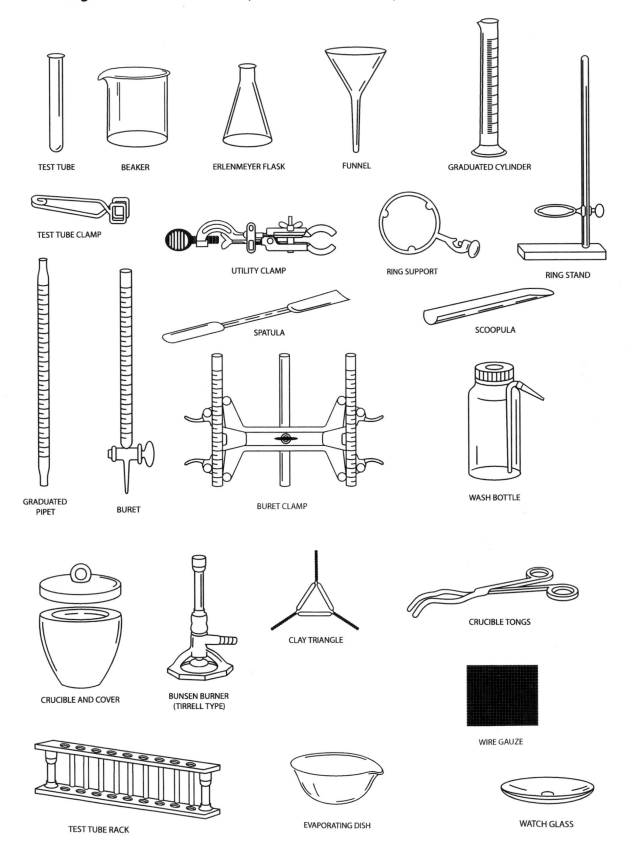

FUNDAMENTAL EXPERIMENTS

I want the answers now or eventually!

—Homer Simpson

EXPERIMENT 1: Accuracy and Precision — Density of a Solid

1.1 Purpose

In experiment 1, the accuracy and precision associated with common laboratory measurements of mass and volume will be evaluated. The density of an unknown solid will be determined by measuring its volume and mass.

1.2 Background

Laboratory experiments frequently require quantitative measurements that are used to determine some overall target quantity. For example, the **density** *d* of some material can be obtained by measuring its mass *m* and volume *V*, equation 1.1:

$$d = m/V \tag{1.1}$$

The ultimate goal of quantitative determinations is to obtain final reliable *quantity values*. Therefore, one needs to know how "reliable" the final determined values actually are. To assess the "reliability" of a certain measurement, information of **accuracy** as well as of **precision** of that particular measurement is required.

The idea of *accuracy* and *precision* is illustrated in the following example. A chunk of gray metal is believed to be either pure iron Fe, $d_{Fe} = 7.87$ g/cm^3, or pure cobalt Co, $d_{Co} = 8.90$ g/cm^3. In principle, measuring the density of the unknown metal provides an answer to the question of the nature that metal. Suppose an experimenter carries out a series of density measurements and obtains an average density value of 8.92 g/cm^3. At first sight, this seems to be good evidence that the unknown metal is cobalt. In terms of *accuracy*, the measured average value of 8.92 g/cm^3 is close to the actual value of 8.90 g/cm^3 for the density of cobalt. If the precision of the density determination were ±0.05 g/cm^3, it is very reasonable to conclude that the metal is indeed cobalt. On the other hand, if the precision of the density measurement were ±1.83 g/cm^3, then one cannot draw any definitive conclusion which metal is present. Both the density of cobalt as well as the density of iron fall into the range of densities defined by the average density value and its deviation, 7.09 g/cm^3 < *d* < 10.75 g/cm^3.

In a similar manner, new and/or competing scientific theories are often tested by measuring physical properties predicted by independent theories; different theories may predict different values. Only very precise and accurate measurements allow one to disregard one theory, or favor another. Quantitative measurements, alone or combined by use of an equation to obtain some derived quantity, are of little value if one cannot qualify their reliability range.

It is important to clearly distinguish between the terms **precision** and **accuracy**. *Accuracy* describes how close the measured value of a quantity comes to the "true" or accepted value of that same quantity. *Precision*, on the other hand, refers to the degree of reproducibility in a series of the same measurements. The three targets shown in Figure 1-1 represent shots of different accuracy and precision.

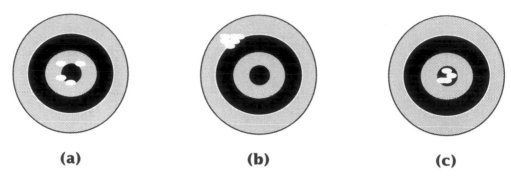

(a)　　　　　　　**(b)**　　　　　　　**(c)**

Figure 1-1: Target shots of different accuracy and precision.

The shots on target (a) are accurate, they all come close to the bull's eye, but they are not very precise. The shots on target (b) are precise, since they are all close to each other, but not very accurate. The shots on target (c) are both precise and accurate.

It is important to note that the precision of this series of shots can be assessed even if the concentric bull's eye pattern is not shown for each. The "bull's eye pattern" is necessary only when the accuracy of the shots has to be evaluated. In most "real world" experiments, however, the "bull's eye pattern", that is the known result, is not available; in fact, obtaining it is the object of the experiment. Therefore, one can only try to infer accuracy from knowable precision. Usually, the greatest precision can be associated with the greatest accuracy, but this assumes that there is no *systematic error* made in the measurements.

All laboratory experiments are subject to error. While good methods, a sound laboratory practice, and attention to detail can help minimize error, it cannot be entirely eliminated. Thus, rather than manipulatively suggesting that there are no errors in an experiment, one should try to identify sources of error in experiments, and suggest how these errors might be reduced. There are two types of error in laboratory measurements. A **systematic error** is an error which occurs regularly due to an inherent flaw in the measuring device. For example, a scale or balance might consistently measure 1.52g too low. Therefore, a *systematic error* affects the *accuracy* of a result. A **random error** refers to the irreproducibility of replicate measurements. Thus, a *random error* affects the *precision* of a result.

Rather than just stating that a result is accurate or precise, it is desirable to be able to describe exactly *how* accurate or precise a particular result is. This can be done through a variety of statistical tools. Most often used are **percent error** *%E*, **standard deviation** *S.D.*, and **relative standard deviation** *R.S.D.*

The **percent error** *%E* describes the *accuracy* of a result, and applies to a single measurement. It is based on the difference between a measured or experimental value and an accepted or theoretical value, equation 1.2:

$$\%E = \frac{|\text{experimental value} - \text{theoretical value}|}{\text{theoretical value}} \times 100\%$$

(1.2)

There are various ways in which equation 1.2 can be used. For example, if averages of all measurements are used to obtain an *experimental* value, and if it is possible to obtain a *theoretical* value, then one can assess the accuracy error for a particular set of measurements. The theoretical value can be obtained, for example, from calculations. Accepted values that are published in the literature, and that are deemed reliable can also be adopted as theoretical values. Very often, however, the *theoretical* value in a *real* experiment is not known in advance.

Equation 1.2 can also be used to assess the error of a particular measurement x_i out a series of measurements. If one takes the theoretical value to be the average or mean value for all the individual measurements, then equation 1.2 can provide the deviation from the mean for any particular measurement x_i.

The **standard deviation** S.D. describes the *precision* of a series of individual measurements in quantitative terms. Although it is a well defined statistical function, it is often used in an ambiguous manner. The most common measure is given in equation 1.3:

$$S.D. = \sqrt{\frac{1}{n-1}\sum_{i=1}^{n}(x_i - \bar{x})^2} \tag{1.3}$$

The standard deviation applies to a series of measurements with n total measurement trials. The value of the ith trial is x_i. The average value $\bar{X}$ for the n individual measurements is given in equation 1.4.

$$\bar{X} = \frac{1}{n}\sum_{i=1}^{n}x_i \tag{1.4}$$

The standard deviation can be thought of representative of the average deviation from the mean value in a series of measurements.

The **relative standard deviation** R.S.D. simply re-expresses S.D. as a percentage of the mean measured value over all the trials, equation 1.5.

$$R.S.D. = \frac{S.D.}{\bar{x}} \times 100\% \tag{1.5}$$

If we assume that the mean value of all trials *also* represents the true value of the quantity, then the expressions for *S.D.* and *R.S.D.* given in equations 1.3 and 1.5 then would provide direct indications of accuracy error.

1.3 Procedure

In experiment 1, we will use a variety of instruments of different precision to determine masses and volumes, such as a triple beam balance and an analytical balance for masses, and beakers, graduated cylinders, volumetric pipets and burets for volumes. We will then use these instruments to determine the density of an unknown solid to a certain degree of accuracy and precision.

1.3.1 Measuring mass

Mass m describes the quantity of matter in an object. Note that mass m is not the same as weight w. As stated in Newtonian physics, the gravitational acceleration g at the surface of the earth acts on a mass m to produce a weight, equation 1.6.

$$w = m \times g \tag{1.6}$$

As long as g maintains a constant value, w will always scale with m. As a consequence, there is — probably unfortunate but also convenient — the practice of applying mass units such as grams and kilograms to weighing measurements with balances. Technically, it would only be correct to describe weights in force units, but since w and m scale with one another, the terms weight and mass are often used synonymously.

1.3.1.1 *Operating a triple beam balance:* The triple beam balance, named for the three beams which carry weights, is rugged, inexpensive, and easy to use. The downside is that it has a precision range of only around 0.1g.

The operating principle of the Triple Beam Balance is simple: It has a beam which is supported by a fulcrum. On one side is a pan on which the object is placed. On the other side, the beam is split into three parallel beams, each supporting one weight. When the weight of an object is measured, each of the three weights can be slid along the beam to increase their lever arm. The mass of the object weighed is the sum of the masses on the three beams A, B, and C which offsets the mass of the object.

Beam A: The middle beam reads only in 100 g increments.

Beam B: The far beam reads only in 10 g increments.

The weights in each of the beams A and B must always sit in a "notch". They cannot be placed at arbitrary points on the beam.

Beam C: The weight on the front beam can be placed to read continuously from 0 to 10 grams. This beam is divided in tenths of a gram, so that an object can be accurately measured to tenths.

Be sure the balance is zeroed before placing anything on the weighing pan. This means that when the weights on all of the beams are placed at zero, the pointer of the balance centers on zero. If the balance is not zeroed, adjust the zero knob until the pointer swings an equal distance on either side of the zero mark.

Carefully place the object to be weighed on the pan. The pointer will move up to the higher part of the scale. Move the weight on the 100 g beam to the largest setting that allows the pointer to stay on the higher part of the scale. Adding 100 more grams will over-tip the scale and the pointer will slide to the lower part of the scale. Repeat this procedure for the 10 g beam. Finally, move the weight on the 1.0 g scale until the pointer rests directly on zero or swings equally on either side of the zero. The final weight will be the combined weights from all three beams.

1.3.1.2. *Measuring masses with a triple beam balance:* Weigh an object that has a mass less than 100 g, such as a pen, a pencil, or a piece of jewelry, using the triple beam balance. Record the mass and a *brief* description of the object in your laboratory notebook.

1.3.1.3 *Operating an analytical balance:* Whereas triple beam balances are precise to around 0.1 g, analytical balances are precise to additional orders of magnitude. Analytical balances are more delicate than triple beam balances, and must be handled with care, and *cleaned after each use*. The balance pan is often placed inside a windowed enclosure to isolate the balance from drafts in the room. The analytical balance should also be placed on a sturdy, level table free from vibrations. Analytic balances are often digital or electronic balances; older types of balances are analog or mechanical balances. The use of the electronic balance is self explanatory. Instructions for using a Mettler mechanical balance appear below.

To zero the instrument, make sure the window of the balance reads zeroes across the scale. Turn the bottom lever from "off" to "weigh" and notice whether a line on the far right of the window coincides with the mark left of "g". If it does not, adjust the upper right hand knob, marked "0" in red, until it does. Your instrument is now zeroed. This knob is also used for tarring. This means that, if you do not want to include the weight of your weighing paper or container (see section 1.3.1.5), you may turn this knob until the scale reads zero with the paper or container on the pan. Not every Mettler balance tares adequately, so you must keep a record of the weight of your paper or container.

When the instrument is zeroed and/or tarred, turn the lever back to "off" and carefully place the object to be weighed on the balance pan. Close the chamber door. Never put the lever immediately on weigh. "Reweigh" it by turning the lever to the right. This will give you an idea of the weight range of your object. When an object weighs less than the balance weights, the middle scale on the window will have two columns of numbers, one white and one green, indicating that more weight needs to be added. When too much weight has been added, the middle scale on the window will move down through zero to an empty screen. Go back to your previous weight and proceed to the lower weight scale.

The knob adjustments for 1 g and 10 g increments are located to the left on the face of the instrument. The knob for less than 1 gram is located on the upper right side of the instrument. As with zeroing, a line needs to coincide with the horizontal mark left of the "g" on the window. When this happens, the weight is read directly off the window of the instrument. Because this is a German instrument, the comma stands in place of a decimal point. Turn the lever back to the off position, remove your object, and return the scale to zeroes.

1.3.1.4 Measuring masses with an analytical balance: Determine the mass of the object you have weighed in section 1.3.1.2, now using an analytical balance. Record the mass in your laboratory notebook.

1.3.1.5 Measuring mass of chemicals: Most chemicals we will use in lab are powders or even liquids and therefore require a container for measurement of mass. *Do not* place a chemical sample directly on the balance pan as this could cause damage to the balance, contaminate your chemical sample and would make it very difficult to transfer the entire sample to any other container for chemical analysis. In our laboratory we will use weighing paper to measure out the mass of powders, and beakers or bottles to measure out the mass of liquids. In order to avoid contamination, you should not re-use weighing paper, and use a clean and dry beaker when measuring masses of liquids.

Mass measurements often employ a technique called *weighing by difference*. When placing a container and substance on the balance pan, the resulting mass is the sum of the mass of the container and the mass of the chemical. Therefore, to measure the mass of a chemical, two mass measurements are needed; one of the container and the chemical and one of the container alone. The mass of the chemical is the difference between these values.

Use a clean spatula when obtaining a solid sample from a reagent bottle. Replace the lid to the bottle when you are finished. When transferring a solid into a container with a narrow opening, use a piece of creased weighing paper. Gently tap the paper to transfer the solid.

There are certain other rules that should always be followed when weighing a chemical substance:

1) Do not weigh hot objects. Convection currents can exert a buoyant force on the balance pan and object which can lead to an incorrect reading of the object's mass. Allow samples to cool to room temperature prior to weighing.

2) Accidents do sometimes happen and cause a chemical spill on or near the balance. It is extremely important that you immediately clean up any chemical spill on or near the balance.

3) When a high degree of accuracy is required, avoid touching the sample container with your hands. Oil from your fingers can be transferred to the container and affect the measured mass.

1.3.2 Measuring volume

Volume is commonly measured by using a graduated cylinder, buret, pipet, or volumetric flask. Beakers are not suitable for measuring exact volumes in the lab since they generally are not very accurate. The one hundred milliliter graduated cylinder measures volumes to tenths of a milliliter. The pipet and the buret can measure volumes to hundredths of a milliliter and are used when a higher degree of accuracy is required. Read volumes with your eye at the level of liquid surface to avoid an error due to parallax. A column of liquid will exhibit a curved surface, or meniscus. The volume of your liquid is the volume read from the bottom of the meniscus as shown in Figure 1-2.

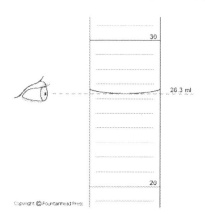

Figure 1-2: Reading Volumes.

Different devices are used to measure volumes of water. We will determine the mass of measured volume of water by using the technique known as *weighing by difference*. In your notebook, set up the following table in which you will enter the results obtained in the next sections.

measured volume	Mass of beaker		Mass of Water
	Empty	Full	
beaker: 20 mL			
graduated cylinder: 5 mL			
graduated cylinder: 50 mL			
pipet: 25.0 mL			
Buret: 25.00 mL			

The accuracy of different volume measuring devices can be judged by comparing the measured volume with an actual volume calculated from the mass and density of water. Since the density of water depends on temperature, record the current room temperature in your laboratory notebook.

1.3.2.1. Measuring volume with a beaker Obtain a 50 mL beaker and determine its mass to the nearest milligram. Record the value in your lab notebook. Using the marks on the beaker as your guide, add 20 mL of water to the beaker and record the mass of the water plus the beaker in your lab notebook. Find the mass of the water according to the *weighing by difference* procedure.

1.3.2.2 Measuring volume with a graduated cylinder: Add 5.0 mL of water to a 10 mL graduated cylinder and 50.0 mL to your 100 mL graduated cylinder. Record the volumes in your laboratory notebook. Next, obtain two 50 mL beakers, label the beakers, and record their mass in your lab notebook. Add the water from the 10 mL graduated cylinder to one beaker and the water from the 100 mL graduated cylinder to the other beaker. Reweigh both beakers and record the masses in your laboratory notebook.

1.3.2.3 Measuring volume with a volumetric pipet: Volumetric pipets have a calibration mark and are used to deliver specific volumes of liquids with high accuracy. To pipet a liquid, the pipet should first be rinsed with distilled water and then with small volumes of the liquid to be dispensed. To do this, a small amount of the liquid should be drawn into the pipet and the pipet is held almost horizontal with the bench top. The pipet is rolled so that the liquid comes in contact with the entire inner surface of the pipet. The liquid is then drained from the pipet and the procedure is repeated. After washing, the pipet is ready for use. The liquid is drawn into the pipet until the liquid level stands above the calibration mark. The liquid is then allowed to drop to the calibration mark and the hanging drop at the pipets tip is removed with a clean wipe. The liquid is then allowed to drain into the desired container. After all the liquid drains, touch the pipet tip to the inside surface of the container to remove the hanging drop. *Do not blow out* any liquid left in the pipet, as the pipet was calibrated to account for the solution that remains in the tip. Use a pipet bulb, *do not* pipet using your mouth. Figure 13 illustrates the proper use of a volumetric pipet.

Using a pipet requires some practice, and you should exercise your technique a few times before measuring volumes with a pipet. Then obtain a 50 mL beaker, and record its mass. With a 25 mL pipet, transfer exactly 25.0 mL of water from a larger beaker into the 50 mL beaker. Record the mass of the beaker plus water in your lab notebook and find the mass of the water alone by subtraction.

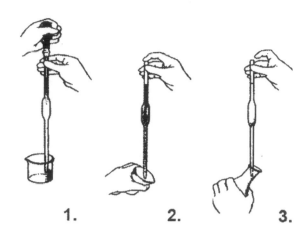

Figure 1-3: Using a volumetric pipet

1.3.2.4 Measuring volume with a buret

Burets are special pieces of equipment that are designed to dispense a quantity of a liquid. Most burets are 50 mL size, meaning that they can deliver, to the nearest 0.05 mL, 50 mL of a liquid to another container such as a beaker or an Erlenmeyer flask. They are marked in tenths of a milliliter increments, and the user estimates whether the level of the meniscus is exactly at one mark, or half-way in-between two marks. Burets are read from top to bottom. When they are filled to the top line the user records the level as being 0.00 mL. This represents the *initial level*. The *final level* is then noted after the desired amount of liquid has been released out of the buret. The difference between the two levels is the volume of liquid that has been delivered to the other container. It is important to note that it is not necessary to start at an initial level of exactly 0.00 mL. The amount that is dispensed can always be accurately determined by the *difference* between starting and final point.

The stopcock at the bottom of the buret can be turned such that the flow of liquid out of the buret can be controlled. That coupled with the very small tip at the bottom of the buret lets the user have good control over just how much liquid is delivered at any one time. As with the pipets, burets should be washed with de-ionized water and the same solution to be used prior to their use. Additionally, you should make sure that the air in the tip of the buret is removed before dispensing liquid.

At this point, obtain a 50 mL buret, fill it with water, and set it up with the buret clamp and stand. Then obtain a 50 mL beaker and record its mass. Using the buret, dispense 25.00 mL into the 50 mL beaker. Re-weigh the beaker and record the combined mass of water and beaker in your notebook.

1.3.3 Density of a solid

To determine the density of a solid, both the mass and the volume of a sample of the solid are needed. We will determine the mass by weighing by difference. The volume is obtained using an indirect displacement procedure. The procedure for determining the density is outlined below:

i) Weigh and record the mass of your 10 mL measuring cylinder.

ii) Fill your measuring cylinder with pellets of an unknown solid approximately up to the 2.0 mL mark.

iii) Re-weigh your measuring cylinder and determine the mass of the unknown solid by subtraction.

iv) Obtain a 50 mL buret, fill it with water, and set it up with the buret clamp. Record the initial reading. With the buret, fill the measuring cylinder containing the unknown solid exactly to the 5.0 mL mark. Record the final reading. The volume of the solid is obtained as 5.0 mL minus the difference between initial and final reading.

v). *Repeat* the procedure *two additional times.*

Set up the following table in your notebook in which you will record your results:

	Empty Cylinder	Filled Cylinder	Buret initial	Buret final
Trial #1				
Trial #2				
Trial #3				

1.4 Calculations

In your calculations, make sure you report your results with the correct number of significant digits. Not all of volume measuring techniques employed produce data of the same precision. Refer to section A.2.8 for the calculation of averages and standard deviations.

1.4.1 Measuring volume

Convert the mass of water you have measured in the different trials of section 1.3.2 into volume by using the density of water, equation 1.7:

$$V_{H_2O} = m_{H_2O}/d_{H_2O} \qquad (1.7)$$

You obtain the mass of water m_{H_2O} from the difference of the mass of the beaker filled with water and the mass of the empty beaker. The density of water is temperature dependent. Refer to your temperature reading, and use Table 1.1 to obtain the corresponding density value d_{H_2O}:

Table 1.1: Density of water at different temperatures.

Temp. (°C)	Density (g/mL)	Temp. (°C)	Density (g/mL)
15	0.9991	24	0.9973
16	0.9990	25	0.9971
17	0.9988	26	0.9968
18	0.9986	27	0.9965
19	0.9984	28	0.9962
20	0.9982	29	0.9960
21	0.9980	30	0.9957
22	0.9978	31	0.9954
23	0.9976	32	0.9951

In your report, include one sample calculation in which you show in detail how to obtain the calculated volume and the percent error. Perform these calculations for all trials, and report your results in form of a table.

The volume obtained when measuring with a beaker, graduated cylinder, pipet or buret is referred to as the *measured volume*. The volume you obtain from the mass of water is referred to as *calculated volume*. For each volume determination, report the percent error %E between the measured volume and the calculated volume. Calculate %E as described in equation 1.2. The *measured volume* corresponds to the *experimental value*, whereas the *calculated volume* corresponds to the *theoretical value*.

Table for section 1.4.1

Measured Volume	Calculated Volume	% Error
Beaker: 20 mL		
Graduated Cylinder: 5 mL		
Graduated Cylinder: 50 mL		
Pipet: 25.0 mL		
Buret: 25.00 mL		

1.4.2 Density of a solid

For each of your three trials, calculate a value for the density of the unknown solid. Set up a table in which you report your results:

	m (g)	V (mL)	d(g/cm³)
Trial #1			
Trial #2			
Trial #3			

In your report, include one sample calculation in which you show in detail how to obtain the mass, the volume and the density.

Calculate an average density, equation 1.4, and the standard deviation, equation 1.3. You might also use the statistical functions of your pocket calculator, or use the statistical functions of a spreadsheet such as Excel. In this case, make a note in your report how the average and standard deviation were obtained.

Based on your density value, identify the nature of the unknown solid. Densities for various metals are collected in Table 1.2.

Table 1.2: Density (in g/cm³) of selected metals

Aluminum (Al):2.7	Tin (Sn): 7.3	Lead (Pb): 11.3
Titanium (Ti): 4.5	Iron (Fe): 7.8	Palladium (Pd) 12.0
Vanadium (V) 6.1	Copper (Cu): 8.9	Tungsten (W): 19.3
Zinc (Zn) 7.1	Silver (Ag): 10.5	Platinum (Pt): 21.1

1.5 Discussion

Incorporate the following points into your discussion. Elaborate on the advantages and disadvantages of each of the volumetric methods that you have examined. Which method is most accurate? When transferring the liquid from the graduated cylinder to the beaker to measure its mass, does this step introduce a systematic and/or random error into the mass measurement?

When you determine the nature of the unknown solid, also consider the standard deviation of your experiment. Out of the list of selected metals, some are close in density, and the assignment might not be unambiguous.

EXPERIMENT 2: Chemical Reactions I — Basic Types of Reaction

2.1 Purpose

In experiment 2, four different types of inorganic reactions are investigated, and the observations are supported by balanced chemical equations.

2.2 Background

Chemists have identified millions of different compounds, and the number of chemical reactions that can be carried out is without limit. However, there are only a few basic types of reactions that represent most any reaction one is likely to encounter. The chemicals change, but the reactions follow similar patterns. Classification of chemical reactions brings order into their overwhelming amount, and makes them easier to study and understand.

Commonly used are two different classification schemes, one that focuses on the way how atoms or group of atoms are reorganized during a reaction (group I), and one that focuses on essential characteristics of a chemical reactions (group II).

Four reaction types belong to group I, all of which involve a step of bond breakage and/or bond formation:

i) **Synthesis** — Two or more substances combine to make a more complex substance: A + B → AB

ii) **Decomposition** — One substance is broken down into two or more simpler substances: AB → A + B

iii) **Single Displacement** — A more *active* element replaces a less *active* element: A +BC → AB + C

iv) **Double Displacement** — Two compounds swap partners and form two new compounds: AB + CD → BC + AD

The four reaction types are also known by different names: Synthesis and decomposition are also called combination and analysis, displacement is also called replacement, and double displacement is also referred to as metathesis reaction. Whatever name people choose to use, the reaction essentials remain the same.

Reactions that belong to group II are characterized by common reaction principles. Examples are

i) **Precipitation Reaction** — Formation of a solid during the course of a chemical reaction

ii) **Redox Reaction** — Change of oxidation states during the course of a chemical reaction.

iii) **Acid-Base Reaction** — Protons H^+ and/or hydroxide ions OH^- take part in a chemical reaction.

iv) **Combustion** — Molecular oxygen O_2 takes part in a chemical reaction.

Most reactions can be classified as both belonging to a reaction scheme of group I as well as of group II. Many reactions also classify as more than one group II reaction type. The preferred classification depends on the most important aspect of a particular reaction a researcher wants to emphasize.

We now discuss the four types of reaction that we will encounter in experiment 2 in more detail.

2.2.1 Precipitation reaction: Precipitation is the formation of a solid out of a solution during a chemical reaction. When the reaction occurs, the solid formed is called the **precipitate**, and the liquid remaining above the solid is called the supernate.

The reaction of aqueous solutions of silver nitrate $AgNO_3$(aq) and sodium chloride NaCl(aq) represents a prototypical precipitation reaction. Silver nitrate and sodium chloride are very soluble ionic compounds and exist as ions in aqueous solution. When an aqueous solution of silver nitrate is mixed with an aqueous solution of sodium chloride, an insoluble white solid forms; equation 2.1

$$AgNO_3(aq) + NaCl(aq) \rightarrow NaNO_3(aq) + AgCl(s), \tag{2.1}$$

The precipitate is silver chloride, an ionic compound that is only sparingly soluble in water. Precipitation reactions are also referred to as *metathesis* or *double displacement* reactions.

The ionic equation for this reaction explicitly shows the ions present in solution; equation 2.2:

$$Ag^+(aq) + NO_3^-(aq) + Na^+(aq) + Cl^-(aq) \rightarrow Na^+(aq) + NO_3^-(aq) + AgCl(s) \tag{2.2}$$

Sodium cation and nitrate anion are *spectator* ions, or ions that remain unchanged in the reaction. These are often eliminated from the ionic equation to give the net ionic equation; equation 2.3:

$$Ag^+(aq) + Cl^-(aq) \rightarrow AgCl(s) \tag{2.3}$$

The formation of a precipitate can be predicted by referring to a set of well-defined solubility rules for ionic compounds in water.

2.2.2 Redox reaction: In a *reduction-oxidation* or *redox* reaction, electrons are transferred from one species to another. For example, in the reaction of sodium metal with chlorine, one electron is lost from each sodium atom Na and one electron is gained by each chlorine atom in Cl_2 to form the ionic compound NaCl. Sodium is oxidized, while chlorine is reduced. This redox reaction is shown in equation 2.4:

$$2 \, Na(s) + Cl_2(g) \rightarrow 2 \, NaCl(s) \tag{2.4}$$

In this example the transfer of electrons is readily recognizable by the change in charge from neutral Na and Cl atoms to the ions Na^+ and Cl^- present in NaCl. As a rule, redox reactions can be recognized by changes in the *oxidation states* of some of the species involved in the reaction. Oxidation states are numbers assigned to elements in compounds for purposes of keeping track of electrons.

Combustion reactions, in which compounds react with molecular oxygen O_2, are also examples of redox reactions. In combustion reactions, often a hydrocarbon is burned in the presence of oxygen gas to form carbon dioxide and water, such as in the Bunsen burner reaction, and the combustion of methane is shown in equation 2.5:

$$CH_4(g) + 2\ O_2(g) \rightarrow CO_2(g) + 2\ H_2O(g) \tag{2.5}$$

Here, carbon undergoes an increase in oxidation state from -IV in CH_4 to +IV in CO_2. *Carbon is oxidized.* Oxygen undergoes a reduction in oxidation state from ±0 in O_2 to -II in CO_2 and H_2O. *Oxygen is reduced.*

A redox reaction, in which one element displaces another element in a compound, can also be classified as *single displacement reaction*. For example, lead will displace copper from copper(II) sulfate in aqueous solution; equation 2.6:

$$Pb(s) + CuSO_4(aq) \rightarrow PbSO_4(aq) + Cu(s) \tag{2.6}$$

Lead is said to be *more active* than copper. A metal can replace any other metal that has a lower activity from a compound. More active metals vigorously react with hydrochloric acid and produce molecular hydrogen H_2; less active metal do not react with HCl.

2.2.3 Synthesis: In a synthesis reaction, two or more substances combine to form one product. For example, lead can be heated with sulfur to form lead sulfide, equation 2.7:

$$8\ Pb(s) + S_8(s) \rightarrow 8\ PbS(s) \tag{2.7}$$

Note that this reaction can also be classified as oxidation-reduction reaction: Lead is oxidized, and sulfur is reduced.

2.2.4 Decomposition. A decomposition reaction occurs when one substance breaks down into simpler substances. For example, calcium carbonate decomposes to form calcium oxide and carbon dioxide gas when heated, equation 2.8:

$$CaCO_3(s) \rightarrow CaO(s) + CO_2(g) \tag{2.8}$$

2.3 Procedure

The reactions described in the sections below produce a sizeable amount of chemical waste. Remember to dispose of waste in the appropriate waste container.

2.3.1 Synthesis of copper sulfide:

The following outlines the procedure for the preparation of copper sulfide. In your notebook, describe the original appearances of the copper and sulfur, and describe the appearance of the product. Also record the observations you make for this synthesis reaction.

i) Clean a crucible and its cover. It is not necessary for the crucible to be perfectly clean, as long as it has been sufficiently heated before a sample is placed in it.

ii) Mount the crucible on a clay triangle on a ring stand. Gently heat the crucible for about 3 minutes and then vigorously for another 3 minutes. Allow the crucible to cool in a gentle flame for a minute, and then remove the crucible by using crucible tongs and allow it to cool to room temperature. Determine the mass of the crucible to the nearest 0.01 g Carry the crucible with the aide of your tongs, and hold a wire gauze beneath it for added support when you transport it to be weighed.

iii) Add a small amount of light copper turnings or copper powder — about 0.25 g — to the crucible and determine the mass of the copper to the nearest 0.01 g. Cover the copper with sulfur. You will use approximately 0.5 g sulfur. that Since excess sulfur will burn off, its mass does not need to be carefully measured. If you use copper powder, mix the copper and sulfur with a *clean* spatula. Make sure that no copper remains on the spatula.

iv) *In the hood*, heat the crucible with the cover slightly cracked open until sulfur fumes are no longer evolved. Cool.

v) Remove the lid and observe the product. If the copper sulfide is not homogeneous, cover again with sulfur and repeat step *iv.*

vi) Weigh the crucible and product, and determine the mass of the product to the nearest 0.01 g.

2.3.2 Decomposition of potassium chlorate:

Place about 1 g of potassium chlorate ($KClO_3$) into a test tube. Carefully heat the test tube with a Bunsen burner. Take care not to allow the $KClO_3$ to spill over or get near the flame. Test for the evolution of oxygen by lighting a wooden splint, blowing it out and inserting it down into the test tube. Do not drop the splint into the test tube. Oxygen is present if the splint glows. If no oxygen was evolved, heat the test tube again for a longer period of time. Test again for oxygen.

2.3.3 Redox-displacement Reactions:

Use about 5 mL of solution per sample, and prepare

• four test tubes containing 2.0 M HCl

• three test tubes containing 0.02 M $CuSO_4$

• two test tubes containing 0.02 M $ZnSO_4$

• one test tube containing 0.02 M $MgSO_4$

• one test tube containing 0.02 M $AgNO_3$

Set up a chart for each test tube that includes what was added, whether or not a reaction took place, and a description of the reaction. Some reactions take longer than others, so allow a minimum of five minutes for the reaction to occur. You might want to use a table such as the one shown below:

Solution	Reaction when Zn is added	Reaction when Mg is added	Reaction when Fe is added	Reaction when Cu is added
2.0 M HCl				
0.02 M $CuSO_4$				-
0.02 M $ZnSO_4$	-	-		
0.02 M $MgSO_4$		-	-	-
0.02 M $AgNO_3$	-	-	-	

Add small pieces of metal to the test tubes and

• test HCl solutions for reaction with Zn, Mg, Fe, and Cu

- test $CuSO_4$ solutions for reaction with Zn, Mg, and Fe
- test $ZnSO_4$ solutions for reaction with Cu and Fe.
- test $MgSO_4$ solution for reaction with Zn.
- test $AgNO_3$ solution for reaction with Cu.

2.3.4 Precipitation Reactions:

Combine the following pairs of reactants in test tubes by using the stock solutions in the lab. Use about 1-2 mL of each solution. Describe each reaction.

$(NH_4)_2CO_3(aq) + CaCl_2(aq) \rightarrow$

$(NH_4)_2CO_3(aq) + K_2SO_4(aq) \rightarrow$

$Ba(NO_3)_2(aq) + CaCl_2(aq) \rightarrow$

$Ba(NO_3)_2(aq) + K_2SO_4(aq) \rightarrow$

2.4 Calculations

2.4.1 Synthesis of copper sulfide:

From your data, calculate the mole ratio of copper and sulfur in copper sulfide as prepared in this experiment. It is stated in the literature that copper combines with sulfur in a mole ratio of roughly 1.8:1 or 9:5, when prepared directly from the elements. Compare your result with the literature result.

2.4.2 Decomposition of potassium chlorate:

Potassium chlorate decomposes into potassium chloride and oxygen. Write a balanced equation for this reaction and decide if this decomposition is a redox reaction.

2.4.3 Displacement Reactions:

Write balanced equations for each reaction carried out in section 2.3.3. Write down reactants and products, and if no reaction occurred, write *N.R.* after the arrow. The most common oxidation state for Cu is Cu^{2+}. For iron, the reaction to form Fe^{3+} is slow, so Fe^{2+} is usually the ion that is observed first.

Arrange the metals zinc Zn, magnesium Mg, iron Fe, copper Cu, and silver Ag in the order of decreasing activity, from the most active to the least active.

According to the activity series derived above, predict the products of the following reactions. Balance the equations, and if no reaction occurs, indicate this by writing *N.R.*

$Mg(s) + ZnSO_4(aq) \rightarrow$

$Ag(s) + HCl(aq) \rightarrow$

$Ag(s) + FeCl_2(aq) \rightarrow$

$Zn(s) + AgNO_3(aq) \rightarrow$

$Ag(s) + CuSO_4(aq) \rightarrow$

2.4.4 Precipitation Reactions:

Write balanced molecular equations and balanced net ionic equations for the four reactions. Include designations for state of matter, e.g. (aq) and (s). Write *N.R.* if no reaction occurred.

2.5 Discussion

In your discussion, address the following points:

1. For the synthesis of copper sulfide, describe how the following errors would affect your result. a) The crucible was still hot when the mass of the copper sulfide compound was determined. b) The contents of the crucible were not homogenous at the end of the reaction; a substantial amount of yellow powder remained.

2. For the redox-displacement reactions, describe how you determined the reactivity order. For example, metal X was able to displace metal Y, thus X is more active than Y. Metal Y reacted vigorously with HCl, whereas metal Z reacted slowly with HCl. Thus, Y is more active than Z, and X is more active than Y and Z.

EXPERIMENT 3: Chemical Composition — Oxides and Hydrates

3.1 Purpose

In experiment 3, various aspects of chemical composition of compounds will be examined. The mass percentage composition of a chemical compound will be determined, and the composition of a hydrated ionic salt in terms of water and ionic component will be analyzed.

3.2 Background

The law of constant composition states that the elemental composition of a pure compound is always the same, regardless of its source or method of preparation. In this experiment, we will prepare the compound magnesium oxide from its pure elements. The mass percentage composition will then be determined from the mass of the reacted magnesium and the mass of the magnesium oxide product.

Magnesium forms an oxide with empirical formula MgO, which is readily prepared by burning magnesium in air. However, since air consists of nitrogen and oxygen, magnesium nitride Mg_3N_2 is a by-product of the oxide forming reaction. The chemical reactions associated with the combustion of magnesium in air are given in equations 3.1 and 3.2, respectively:

$$2\ Mg + O_2 \rightarrow 2\ MgO \tag{3.1}$$

$$3\ Mg + N_2 \rightarrow Mg_3N_2 \tag{3.2}$$

In order to get a uniform product distribution, magnesium nitride needs to be converted into magnesium oxide. To this end, magnesium nitride is reacted with water. The products of this hydrolysis reaction are magnesium hydroxide $Mg(OH)_2$ and ammonia NH_3, equation 3.3.

$$Mg_3N_2 + 6\ H_2O \rightarrow 3\ Mg(OH)_2 + 2\ NH_3 \tag{3.3}$$

Finally, heating magnesium hydroxide produces magnesium oxide, with the evolution of water H_2O, equation 3.4:

$$2\ Mg(OH)_2 \rightarrow 2\ MgO + 2\ H_2O \tag{3.4}$$

Thus, in a reaction sequence consisting of reactions shown in equations 3.1-3.4, all magnesium initially present is converted into one particular oxide of magnesium, MgO.

Magnesium oxide belongs to the class of **ionic compounds**, which consist of positive and negative ions held together by electrostatic forces of attraction. Ionic compounds in which the hydrogen atoms of acids are replaced by metal ions are referred to as *salts*. Many salts crystallize as **hydrates**. A hydrate is a compound in which a fixed number of water molecules is associated with each formula unit. Many ionic compounds form more than one hydrate. For example, magnesium sulfate $MgSO_4$ exists in a monohydrated form $MgSO_4 \cdot H_2O$, as hexahydrate $MgSO_4 \cdot 6H_2O$ and as heptahydrate $MgSO_4 \cdot 7H_2O$. Magnesium sulfate heptahydrate is commonly known as Epsom salt. Epsom salt is used to reduce inflammation of the skin when applied externally.

In a hydrate, the water can be chemically bound to the cation or anion, or it can be physically trapped within the crystal lattice. If the water is chemically bound to an ion, the compound is referred to as a complex ion. The chemical bonds in complex compounds are weaker than the ionic bonds of electrostatic forces between oppositely charged ions, and as a consequence, water of hydration can often be driven off by heating the hydrate. In this reaction, the *anhydrous* compound is formed and water is liberated. A general equation for this process is shown in equation 3.5:

$$M_yX_x \cdot nH_2O \rightarrow M_yX_x + n\,H_2O \qquad \text{(3.5)}$$

For transition metal compounds, the dehydration process might be accompanied by a change of color. In the crystal environment, the crystal water forms a complex ion with the transition metal cation of characteristic color. When the water is driven out, the complex ion turns into a regular ion which displays its own color.

The number of water molecules in a hydrate is not limited to seven or less than seven, but in cases might even be higher. For example, Sodium tetraborate, also known as Borax, forms a decahydrate with ten waters of hydration, $Na_2B_4O_7 \cdot 10H_2O$. Water of a hydrate compound is also referred to as *crystal water*.

In this experiment, we will determine the mass percentage of magnesium and oxygen in magnesium oxide, and the empirical formula for a hydrate of unknown hydration number.

3.3 Procedure

Although not glowing-red, hot crucibles, rings, tripods, and clay triangles may be hot enough to cause a severe burn. Place your hand near a heated object to feel for the radiation of heat before touching the object. This will prevent severe burns. If you do suffer a burn, immediately immerse the burned area in an ice bath, or cold water.

Tabulate your data neatly. Make certain to list any observations concerning the appearance of magnesium, magnesium oxide, and of the unknown hydrate before and after heating.

3.3.1 Composition of Magnesium Oxide:

The procedure for the preparation of magnesium oxide is outlined in the following steps.

i) Clean a crucible and its cover. It is not necessary for the crucible to be perfectly clean, as long as it has been brought to a *constant mass* (see steps iii and iv) before a sample is placed in it.

ii) Mount the crucible with its cover on a clay triangle on a ring stand. Gently heat the crucible for about 3 minutes and then vigorously for another 3 minutes. Allow the crucible to cool in a gentle flame for a minute; then remove the crucible by using crucible tongs and allow it to cool to room temperature. Do not touch the crucible for the remainder of the experiment, as oils from your skin can affect the mass. Determine the mass of the crucible and cover to the nearest milligram ($1mg = 1\times10^{-3}$ g). When you transport the crucible to be weighed, carry it with your tongs, and hold a wire gauze beneath it for added support.

iii) Heat the crucible a second time for about three minutes. Cool the crucible, and weigh the crucible to the nearest mg. Report the mass in your laboratory notebook.

iv) If the mass of the crucible is not constant to within ±0.002 g, repeat step *iii* until its mass is constant to within ±0.002 g. Report the mass for each measurement in your laboratory notebook.

v) Obtain about 0.3 g of sanded magnesium ribbon. Fold the magnesium into a ball in a loose, open structure and place it into the crucible. Weigh the crucible and contents to the nearest mg.

vi) Place the crucible on a clay triangle mounted on a ring stand. Heat the uncovered crucible, and cover the crucible as quickly as possible after the magnesium ignites. To keep the magnesium burning, slightly raise the cover periodically to admit air. Replace the cover when the magnesium reignites. Continue heating, occasionally raising the cover, until the magnesium no longer burns. Heat the product for about three more minutes with the cover slightly open. Cool the crucible.

vii) Add about ten drops of de-ionized water to the cooled crucible. Reheat the crucible with the cover slightly open. Gently heat the crucible for a few minutes and then vigorously for some additional minutes. Cool the crucible, and weigh the crucible and contents to the nearest mg.

viii) Heat the crucible a second time for about three minutes. Cool the crucible, and weigh the crucible and contents to the nearest mg.

ix) If the mass of the crucible is not constant to within ±0.002 g, repeat step *viii* until its mass is constant to within ±0.002 g. Report the mass for each measurement in your laboratory notebook.

3.3.2 Formula of a hydrate:

The procedure for determining the mass of crystal water in a sample of an unknown hydrate is outlined in the following steps. Record changes in appearance of the compound during the dehydration process. Some crystals undergo a process of thermal decomposition. For example, colorless copper sulfate $CuSO_4$ might decompose and form black copper oxide CuO. When you observe signs of decomposition, remove the crucible from the flame, and continue the dehydration process at reduced heat.

i) Clean a crucible and its cover. It is not necessary for the crucible to be perfectly clean, as long as it has been brought to a *constant mass* (see steps iii and iv) before a sample is placed in it.

ii) Mount the crucible on a clay triangle on a ring stand. Gently heat the crucible for about 3 minutes and then vigorously for another 3 minutes. Allow the crucible to cool in a gentle flame for a minute; then remove the crucible using crucible tongs and allow it to cool to room temperature. Do not touch the crucible for the remainder of the experiment, as oils from your skin can affect the mass. Determine the mass of the crucible and cover to the nearest milligram ($1mg = 1 \times 10^{-3}$ g). When you transport the crucible to be weighed carry the crucible with tongs, and hold a wire gauze beneath it for added support.

iii) Heat the crucible a second time for about three minutes. Cool the crucible, and weigh the crucible to the nearest mg. Report the mass in your laboratory notebook.

iv) If the mass of the crucible is not constant to within ±0.002 g, repeat step *iii* until its mass is constant to within ±0.002 g. Report the mass for each measurement in your laboratory notebook.

v) Retrieve a sample of an unknown hydrate provided. Record the formula of the compound that forms the hydrate in your notebook. Place about 1 g of the hydrate into the crucible, and record the mass to within 1 mg.

vi) Gently heat the crucible on a ring stand for about 3 minutes and then vigorously for 3 to 5 more minutes. Remove the crucible and allow it to cool. Weigh the crucible and its contents to the nearest 1 mg.

vii) Heat the crucible a second time for about three minutes. Cool the crucible, and weigh the crucible and contents to the nearest mg.

viii) If the mass of the crucible is not constant to within ±0.002 g, repeat step *vii* until its mass is constant to within ±0.002 g. Report the mass for each measurement in your laboratory notebook.

3.4 Calculations

Show how all the calculations are performed. In particular, demonstrate how you determine the mass of oxygen present in magnesium oxide, and the mass of water present in the hydrate.

3.3.1 Composition of Magnesium Oxide:

From your data, determine the mass of oxygen that combined with the magnesium, and calculate the mass percentages of magnesium and oxygen in magnesium oxide as prepared in your experiment.

Convert these masses to an amount in moles, write a tentative formula based on the numbers of moles, and divide each subscript of the formula by the smallest subscript. To obtain the empirical formula of magnesium oxide, round off any subscripts that differ only slightly from whole numbers.

From the empirical formula for magnesium oxide calculate the empirical mass percent of oxygen in magnesium oxide. Determine your percent error introduced by rounding off by comparing your experimentally determined mass percent to the empirical mass percent obtained after rounding off.

3.4.2 Formula of a hydrate:

From your data, determine the mass of the water present in your hydrate, the number of moles of water present in your hydrate, and the number of moles of compound present in your hydrate. Determine the formula of your hydrate.

$$.190 \; g \; O_2 \; \frac{1 \; mol \; O_2}{32.00 \; g \; O_2} \; \frac{2 \; mol \; O}{1 \; mol \; O_2} =$$

16

$$.190 \; g \; O_2 \qquad 16 \; g \; O$$

3.5 Discussion

In your discussion, comment on why it is necessary to heat the crucible to constant mass. Explain how the following errors might influence your results: The crucible was still warm when weighed. Some material escaped when the cover of the crucible is raised.

Assess whether or not this experiment could be used to determine the formulas of other oxides. Comment on whether or not this experiment would allow one to determine the formula of the oxides of carbon.

EXPERIMENT 4: Chemical Reactions II — A Cycle of Copper Reactions

4.1 Purpose

In experiment 4, a sample of copper metal is taken through a series of chemical reactions that form a cycle.

4.2 Background

The *cycle of copper reactions* illustrates important principles of chemical reactions and coordination compounds: The metal copper Cu changes its oxidation state from 0 to +2 and back to 0; in a replacement reaction an active metal replaces a less active metal; the coordination compounds and complex ions of copper display their characterize blue color. The cycle involves five reactions, and is illustrated in Figure 4-1:

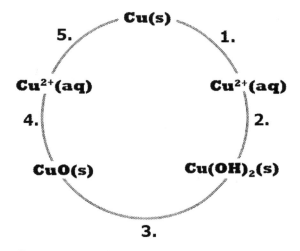

Figure 4-1: A cycle of copper reactions

The cycle begins with elemental copper, which in a first reaction is oxidized to copper(II) cation. Copper(II) is then carried through different solid forms. In the last step, copper(II) cation is reduced, the copper metal is regenerated, and the cycle is closed. In principle it is possible to recover 100% of the initial sample of copper since each reaction in the cycle goes to completion. Your skill in carrying out the procedure quantitatively is reflected in the percent recovery of your copper sample, assuming that your copper product is pure.

The five reactions that lead to the five steps of the cycle of copper reactions are now described in more detail.

Step 1: Copper metal is oxidized to Cu(II) cation, equation 4.1:

$$3\ Cu(s) + 2NO_3^- + 8H^+ \rightarrow 3\ Cu^{2+}(aq) + 4\ H_2O + 2\ NO \tag{4.1}$$

This reaction is written as net ionic equation; the full molecular equations shows that copper(II) nitrate $Cu(NO_3)_2$ is produced:

$$3\ Cu(s) + 8\ HNO_3(aq) \rightarrow 3\ Cu(NO_3)_2(aq) + 4\ H_2O + 2\ NO$$

Nitrogen monoxide NO, a colorless gas, will instantly react with molecular oxygen O_2 from air, and forms gaseous nitrogen dioxide: $2\ NO + O_2 \rightarrow 2\ NO_2$. Nitrogen dioxide is of brown color, and one observes the development of a brown gas during the course of the reaction. The Cu^{2+} ions are hydrated and form the complex ion $[Cu(H_2O)_4]^{2+}$, which gives the resulting solution a light blue color.

Step 2: Cu(II) cation reacts with hydroxide OH⁻ to form copper(II) hydroxide, equation 4.2:

$$Cu^{2+}(aq) + 2\ OH^-(aq) \rightarrow Cu(OH)_2(s) \tag{4.2}$$

Copper(II) hydroxide is insoluble and forms a pale blue precipitate.

Step 3: Black solid copper(II)oxide is formed in a thermal decomposition reaction of copper(II)hydroxide, equation 4.3:

$$Cu(OH)_2(s) \rightarrow CuO(s) + H_2O \tag{4.3}$$

Step 4: Copper(II)oxide is reacted with acid to regenerate the Cu(II) cation, equation 4.4:

$$CuO(s) + 2\ H^+ \rightarrow Cu^{2+}(aq) + H_2O \tag{4.4}$$

The acid used in this step is sulfuric acid H_2SO_4, since copper sulfate $CuSO_4$ is soluble and will not form a precipitate.

Step 5: Copper metal is regenerated by the reduction of Cu^{2+} with zinc, equation 4.5:

$$Cu^{2+}(aq) + Zn(s) \rightarrow Zn^{2+}(aq) + Cu(s) \tag{4.5}$$

4.3 Procedure

Carefully record all of your observations as you perform the experiment. Include the observations on the appearances of solutions and products, the evolution of gases, and any points of difficulty in the procedure which could lead to loss or impurity of product.

Concentrated acids and bases are used in this lab experiment. A single drop can result in permanent damage to your eyes. Take proper precautions when handling these hazardous chemicals!

A ten-step procedure for the copper cycle reaction is outlined below:

i) Obtain about 0.5 g sample of copper wire. Record the mass of the sample to the nearest 0.01 g. Bend the wire so that it will lay flat and place it in a 250 mL beaker.

ii) *In the hood*, add about 4 mL of 16 M nitric acid HNO_3. Concentrated nitric acid is extremely corrosive and must be handled very carefully. Gently swirl the beaker until all of the copper has dissolved.

iii) Slowly add about 30 mL of 3.0 M sodium hydroxide NaOH while stirring the solution. This will neutralize excess HNO_3 and precipitate $Cu(OH)_2$.

iv) Place the beaker on a wire gauze on a ring stand and slowly heat it to a gentle boil with a Bunsen burner. This will convert $Cu(OH)_2$ to CuO. Stir the solution constantly while you are heating it to prevent it from splattering. The reaction is complete when the solution becomes colorless and a black precipitate has settled to the bottom of the beaker.

v) Decant the liquid from the copper oxide precipitate, being careful not to lose any product. Add about 75 mL of hot de-ionized water. Decant the water after the CuO has settled.

vi) Slowly add 15 mL of 6.0 M H_2SO_4 while stirring. The black precipitate of copper oxide will dissolve. The blue color of copper(II) sulfate solutions will appear.

vii) *In the hood*, add about 2.0 g of zinc powder or light zinc turnings and stir. If you use zinc powder, add the zinc powder in small portions to reaction mixture. Zinc sulfate solution is colorless, and the disappearance of the blue color means that all of the Cu^{2+} has reacted. The excess zinc will react with excess H_2SO_4 in the solution, producing hydrogen gas. When the bubbling of hydrogen has ceased, decant the liquid.

viii) Inspect your sample for unreacted zinc. If necessary, add 10 mL of 6 M HCl and warm the solution to dissolve any unreacted zinc. Do not boil. Decant the liquid when the evolution of hydrogen has stopped.

ix) Transfer the copper product to a porcelain dish. Wash the product with 5 mL of de-ionized water and decant. Repeat the washing with de-ionized water two more times. *In the hood*, wash the product with 5 mL of methanol and decant.

x) Dry the product on a hot plate. Determine the mass of the product to the nearest 0.01 g.

4.4 Calculations

Classify the reactions used in the copper cycle. List each reaction, and classify the reactions as synthesis, decomposition, precipitation, displacement, and redox. For oxidation-reduction reactions, state which species is oxidized and which species is reduced. Also include the equation for the reaction of zinc with sulfuric acid. Determine the percent recovery %RC of your copper sample:

$$\%RC = \frac{m_{recovered}}{m_{initial}} \times 100$$

Include the starting amount of copper and the final amount of copper along with the percent recovery of copper for this reaction.

4.5 Discussion

In your discussion, pay special attention to your yield of recovery. If the recovery yield is smaller than 80%, identify the cause for loss of copper. If the recovery yield is larger than a 100%, provide a reasonable explanation for this unreasonable fact.

EXPERIMENT 5: Acid-Base Chemistry I — A Blueberry Indicator

5.1 Purpose

In experiment 5, a pH-indicator based on blueberry juice will be constructed. It will be used to estimate the pH-range of common household items and of over-the-counter medication.

5.2 Background

The concept of pH was first introduced by Danish chemist S. P. L. Sørensen in 1909. The pH-value of a solution serves as a measure of its acidity or alkalinity. Solutions with a pH of less than seven are considered *acidic*, while those with a pH greater than seven are considered *basic* or alkaline. pH 7 is considered neutral because it is the accepted pH of pure water at 25 °C.

The name, pH, has been purported to come from a variety of places including *power* of *Hydrogen* in English. However, pH is actually shorthand for its mathematical approximation: in Chemistry a small p is used in place of writing -**log$_{10}$** and the H, which more correctly should be [H$^+$], stands for concentration of hydrogen cations.

Although pH is formally dependent upon the **activity** of hydrogen cations H+, for pure dilute solutions, the **concentration** or molarity may be used as a substitute with some sacrifice of accuracy. The pH reading of a solution is usually obtained by comparing unknown solutions to those of known pH.

In terms of concentration, pH is defined as follows, equation 5.1:

$$pH = -\log_{10}[H^+] \tag{5.1}$$

The definition of acidic, neutral, or basic solutions is based on the auto-ionization of water, shown in equation 5.2:

$$H_2O \rightleftharpoons H^+ + OH^- \tag{5.2}$$

This process is characterized by its *dissociation constant*, that is the *ion product of water* K_W, equation 5.3:

$$K_W = [H^+]\cdot[OH^-] = 1.0\times10^{-14} \text{ (at 25°C)} \tag{5.3}$$

If the self-ionization of water is the only source of H$^+$ ions, then it follows that [H$^+$] = [OH$^-$], and we have

$$[H^+]\cdot[OH^-] = [H^+]^2 = 1.0\times10^{-14}$$

$$[H^+] = 1.0\times10^{-7}$$

$$\log_{10}[H^+] = -7.0$$

$$pH = 7.0 \tag{5.4}$$

Thus, the pH of pure water is seven, and pure water represents the standard for a neutral solution.

We can further introduce the pOH — in a sense the opposite of pH — which measures the concentration of OH- ions, or the basicity. pOH is defined as follows, equation 5.5:

$$pOH = -\log_{10}[OH^-] \tag{5.5}$$

pH and pOH are linked by the ion product of water K_w, and the following useful relationship can be derived:

$$pH + pOH = 14.0 \tag{5.5}$$

When we want to assess the number of significant figures of pH or pOH values, we have to keep in mind that for logarithms, the only place where significant figures are contained is in the decimal portion. Thus, a pH of 2.02 is reported with an accuracy of two, and not three, significant figures.

This is understandable in light of the fact that logarithms are nothing but exponents, and that the pH — or pOH — is an exponent that gives us the concentration of hydrogen cations or hydroxide anions.

In writing a number such as 0.0095 using normalized scientific notation, we would write 9.5×10^{-3}. The *significand* [9.5] carries the two significant figures, and the exponent [-3] only indicates the position to the right of the decimal point where the first significant figure appears. We can now derive the hydrogen ion concentration of a solution with pH = 2.02 as follows:

$$[H^+] = 10^{-2.02} = 10^{0.98-3} = 10^{0.98} \times 10^{-3} = 9.5 \times 10^{-3} = 0.0095$$

Thus, for the pH value of 2.02, the figure to the left of the decimal point only reflects the number of non-significant zeros.

One way to measure pH values is by addition of a pH indicator into the solution under study. A pH indicator is a *halochromic* compound — a material which changes color when pH changes occur. Therefore, the indicator color varies depending on the pH of the solution. *Qualitative* pH determinations can be made with universal indicators that have broad color variability over a wide pH range. *Quantitative* determinations can be made using indicators that have strong color variability over a small pH range.

In this experiment, we will construct a universal indicator from blueberry juice extract. We will then use this indicator system for a qualitative assessment of the pH of common household articles and over-the counter medication.

5.3 Procedure

5.3.1 Preparation of the blueberry juice extract:

Place 100 mL of water and about a dozen blueberries into a 250 mL beaker. Place the beaker on a wire gauze on a ring stand, and slowly heat it to boil with a Bunsen burner. Continue the process of heating until the initial amount of liquid has been reduced to about 40-50 mL.

Turn off the Bunsen burner, and let the solution cool down. While the solution is cooling down, set up your filtration equipment. This procedure is illustrated in Figure 5-1:

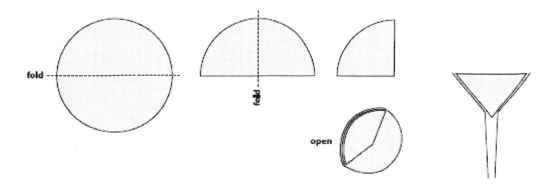

Figure 5-1: Setting up a funnel for filtration

First, fold a round piece of filter paper in half and crease it. Then, fold it again and crease it to produce a quarter circle. One outer layer of paper is separated from the other three (not two and two!) and the opening made wider by lightly squeezing together at the creases. The conical shaped piece of filter paper is placed into a glass or plastic funnel and wetted slightly with de-ionized water from a wash bottle.

Place the funnel with the filter paper in a ring stand clamp. The funnel should sit loosely in the clamp — do not tighten the clamp around the funnel. Filter your blueberry juice extract; you should get at least 15 mL of a bluish-red fruit juice.

5.3.2 Preparation of acid standards

Place five dry and clean 18×150mm test tubes into a test tube rack; label the test tubes 1, 2, 3, 4, and 5.

Add 10.0 mL of 0.1 M hydrochloric acid to your 10 mL graduated cylinder. Transfer 9.0 mL into test tube #1, while 1.0 mL remain in the graduated cylinder.

Fill the graduated cylinder with de-ionized water up to the 10.0 mL mark. Stir the contents of the graduated cylinder with a stirring rod. Transfer 9.0 mL of this solution into test tube #2, while 1.0 mL remain in the graduated cylinder.

Repeat the above procedure three more times in order to produce diluted acid solutions for test tubes #3, #4, and #5.

5.3.3 Preparation of base standards

Place five dry and clean 18×150mm test tubes into a test tube rack; label the test tubes 13, 12, 11, 10, and 9.

Add 10.0 mL of 0.1 M sodium hydroxide solution to your 10 mL graduated cylinder. Transfer 9.0 mL into test tube #13, while 1.0 mL remains in the graduated cylinder.

Fill the graduated cylinder with de-ionized water up to the 10.0 mL mark. Stir the contents of the graduated cylinder with a stirring rod. Transfer 9.0 mL of this solution into test tube #12, while 1.0 mL remains in the graduated cylinder.

Repeat the above procedure three more times in order to produce diluted base solutions for test tubes #11, #10, and #9.

5.3.4 Preparation of the indicator scale

Add 1.0 mL of blueberry juice to each of the 10 test tubes containing the acid and base standards. Shake the test tubes as to mix their contents.

For each test tube, report the color of its solution as precisely as possible. Collect your observations in a table such as the one shown below. The table should have 10 rows. In your table, also include an entry for pH. You will complete this table when doing your calculations.

Test Tube	Color	pH value
#1		
#2		
#3		

5.3.5 Estimating the pH of vinegar:

Place 9.0 mL of clear vinegar into a clean 18×150mm test tube and add 1.0 mL of blueberry juice. Shake the test tube to mix its contents. Precisely record the color of the solution in your lab notebook.

5.3.6 Estimating the pH of Ammonia cleaning solution:

The following steps must be carried out in the hood! Place 9.0 mL of clear Ammonia cleaning solution into a clean 18×150mm test tube and add 1.0 mL of blueberry juice. Shake the test tube to mix its contents. Precisely record the color of the solution in your lab notebook.

5.3.7 Estimating the pH of non prescription medications:

Use a clean 25×200mm test tube, and dissolve a 325mg tablet of Aspirin in 9.0 mL de-ionized water. Gently heat the solution with a Bunsen burner to aid the dissolution process. As the warm solution is cooling down, the *excipient* — the inactive substance used as a carrier for the active ingredients in a tablet — will crystallize out. The active ingredient However will remain in solution. Add 1.0 mL of blueberry juice to your solution, and record the color of your solution in your lab-notebook.

5.3.8 Estimating the pH of an antacid tablet:

Use a clean 25×200mm test tube, and dissolve an antacid tablet that contains between 250mg and 750mg of the active ingredient in 9.0 mL de-ionized water. Gently heat the solution with a Bunsen burner to aid the dissolution process. Upon cooling, excipients, if any, will precipitate, and the active ingredient will remain in solution. Add 1.0 mL of blueberry juice to your solution, and record the color of your solution in your lab-notebook.

5.4 Calculations

5.4.1 pH values of the indicator system

For each of the ten test tubes, calculate the pH value *before* addition of the blueberry extract. Enter the value into the table you have set up for your observation, and report your pH values with an accuracy of *one significant digit*.

Show in sample calculations for one acid and one base standard, how you obtained your pH values. An example is given below:

Test tube #12 – contains [OH⁻] solution

> Initial volume V_{init}: 1.0 mL
>
> Final volume V_{fin}: 10.0 mL
>
> Initial concentration c_{init}: 0.1 M
>
> Final concentration c_{fin}: $c_{fin} = c_{init} \times V_{init}/ V_{fin} = 0.01 M$
>
> $pOH = -\log_{10} 0.01 = 2.0$
>
> $pH = 14.0 - pOH = 12.0$

5.4.2 Accuracy of the indicator system

When 1 mL of blueberry juice extract is added to the initial solutions, the pH will slightly change. Here, we assume that the blueberry juice extract is pH neutral, and that the change in pH is only due to dilution: The initial 9.0 mL of acid or base are diluted to a new volume of 10.0 mL. For one acid and one base standard, show that *within our accuracy of one significant digit*, the pH *does not change* upon addition of the blueberry juice. Calculate the concentrations of H⁺ or OH⁻ and the pH before after addition of 1.0 mL indicator, and compare.

5.4.3 pH range of various samples

Based on your observations, report a pH-range for vinegar, the Ammonia solution, Aspirin, and the antacid. The blueberry indicator is not a highly precise pH system, but a generic universal indicator. We only can make a *qualitative* assessment of pH values, and therefore report a pH range rather than one pH value. For example, if we should measure the pH of orange juice (pH ≈ 3.5) with our indicator system, we would report a pH range of 3.0-4.0.

5.5 Discussion

State the gist of your results. Comment on possible systematic as well as random errors. Assess the accuracy of the blueberry indicator.

The blueberry indicator is but one example of a "natural" universal indicator. Many plant pigments have colors that change with pH. The extract obtained from red cabbage for example is composed of a mixture of component pigments which change color at different pH. As the pH of the solution is changed from 1 to 14, the color changes, following the sequence below:

> red → pink → purple → blue → green → yellow

On a qualitative level, compare the blueberry indicator to the red-cabbage indicator, and point out similarities as well as differences.

EXPERIMENT 6: Thermochemistry I — Specific Heat of Metals

6.1 Purpose

In experiment 6, the specific heat of metals will be determined by using calorimetry.

6.2 Background

Heat capacity C describes how the temperature of a substance changes when it absorbs or releases an amount of heat q. It is defined as the amount of heat required to change the temperature of a substance by 1 °C or 1 K. If an amount of heat q is required to change the temperature of a substance by an amount ΔT, then the heat capacity C is given by:

$$C = \frac{q}{\Delta T}$$

(6.1)

If the size of the sample is increased, a larger amount of heat will have to be absorbed or released to result in the same temperature change ΔT. In other words, heat capacity is an *extensive* property of a substance; its value depends on the amount of substance being considered. Two corresponding *intensive* quantities are also defined, the molar heat capacity C_M and the specific heat capacity or specific heat s. The specific heat capacity is often referred to as c, but we will use the symbol s to avoid possible confusions with the heat capacity C.

The molar heat capacity C_M is the amount of heat required to raise the temperature of one mole of a substance by 1 °C or 1 K. If n denotes the number of moles of substance, then

$$C_M = \frac{q}{n \cdot \Delta T}$$

(6.2)

The specific heat s is the amount of heat required to change the temperature of 1 gram of a substance by 1 °C or 1 K:

$$s = \frac{q}{m \cdot \Delta T}$$

(6.3)

Specific heats commonly carry units of $J \cdot g^{-1}\,°C^{-1}$ or $J \cdot g^{-1}\,K^{-1}$

The specific heats of some substances are given in Table 6.1. Note that water has a very high specific heat, and that the specific heats of metals are low. This means that, if the same amount of heat is added to both 1 g of a metal and 1 g of water, the increase in the temperature of the metal will be much greater than the increase in the temperature of the water. A body of water such as an ocean or a lake can absorb or give off a large quantity of heat with only a small change in temperature.

Table 6-1 Specific heat of water, air and of selected metals

Substance	Specific Heat s/J·g^{-1}·$^\circ$C^{-1}
Water	4.18
Air	1.01
Aluminum	0.90
Iron	0.45
Zinc	0.39
Tin	0.21
Lead	0.13

In this experiment, the specific heat of a metal is measured by using a simple Styrofoam "coffee-cup" calorimeter. A sample of hot metal is added to a calorimeter that contains cool water. Assuming that no heat is dissipated to the surroundings, the heat lost by the hot metal q_m is equal to the heat gained by the cool water q_w and by the Styrofoam cups of the calorimeter q_{cup}. The law of *conservation of energy* leads to the following relation, equation 6.4:

$$- q_m = q_w + q_{cup} \tag{6.4}$$

When thermal equilibrium is reached, the metal, water, and calorimeter share a common final temperature T_f. Using heat capacities C, equation 6.1, the expression of equation 6.4 writes as follows:

$$- C_m \cdot \Delta T_m = C_w \cdot \Delta T_w + C_{cup} \cdot \Delta T_{cup} \tag{6.5}$$

The change in temperature obtained is the difference between initial temperature T_i and final temperature T_f. As stated above, metal, water, and calorimeter will all reach the same final temperature T_f. The initial temperature of the hot metal is given as $T_{i,m}$. Further, the experiment is set up so that the cool water and the calorimeter are at the same initial temperature $T_{i,wc}$. When expressing the heat capacity of the metal C_m in terms of its mass m_m and specific heat s_m, and expressing the heat capacity of the water C_w in terms of its mass m_w and specific heat s_w (compare equation 6.3) we get

$$-s_m \cdot m_m \cdot (T_f\text{-}T_{i,m}) = s_w \cdot m_w \cdot (T_f\text{-}T_{i,wc}) + C_{cup} \cdot (T_f\text{-}T_{i,wc}) \tag{6.6}$$

Since the specific heat of water s_w is known, compare table 6-1, the specific heat of the metal s_m can be calculated from equation 6.6, once the heat capacity of the calorimeter C_{cup} has been measured.

The heat capacity of the calorimeter is determined in a similar experiment. The calorimeter is filled with cool water. The calorimeter and the cool water are at thermal equlibrium, and have the same initial temperature, $T_{i,cw} = T_{i,cup}$. A sample of hot water at a temperature $T_{i,hw}$ is added to it. The heat lost by the hot water is equal to the heat gained by the cool water and by the calorimeter:

$$-q_{hw} = q_{cw} + q_{cup} \tag{6.7}$$

At an equilibrium final temperature T_f, equation 6.7 writes as

$$-s_w \cdot m_{hw} \cdot (T_f\text{-}T_{i,hw}) = s_w \cdot m_{cw} \cdot (T_f\text{-}T_{i,cw}) + C_{cup} \cdot (T_f\text{-}T_{i,cw}) \tag{6.8}$$

The specific heat of water s_w is known, compare table 6-1, and the heat capacity of the calorimeter can be calculated from the experimental data by using equation 6.8.

6.3 Procedure

Temperatures in the calorimeter will be measured by using the accumet® AB15 pH/mV/°C Meter. The samples will be heated in test tubes placed in a beaker of boiling water. The temperature of the water bath will be measured by using a regular thermometer.

6.3.1 Set up of Styrofoam cup calorimeter

A simple type of calorimeter that is suitable for measuring heats of reaction in aqueous solution is the so called *Styrofoam-cup calorimeter.* This term simply refers to a thermally insulated reaction vessel in which a chemical reaction is carried out, such as a Styrofoam cup. The Styrofoam-cup is placed inside a beaker, which provides an additional insulating layer of air. A typical setup of a Styrofoam cup calorimeter is depicted in Figure 6-1:

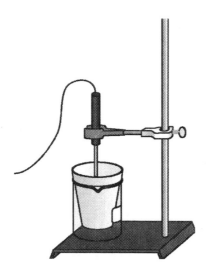

Figure 6-1: Styrofoam cup calorimeter with temperature probe.

Select a large Styrofoam cup (about 450 mL, or two cups, or 16 fl oz) Place the Styrofoam cup into a 600ml beaker, or into a second Styrofoam cup. Arrange the calorimeter and accumet® instrument so that the temperature probe can be conveniently lowered into the Styrofoam cup.

6.3.2 Preparing the samples

Fill two 25x200 mm test tubes with about 30 mL of water. Add about 20g of an unknown metal to a third 25x200 mm test tube, and about 40g of an unknown metal to a fourth 25x200 mm test tube. The metal samples must be dry to obtain good results. Dry your metal on a paper towel if it appears wet.

Place the test tubes into a 600 mL beaker, and add water to the beaker up to the 500 mL mark. Place the beaker on a wire gauze on a ring stand. Heat the water to its boiling point. The water should simmer, but it should not vigorously boil. Adjust the flame of your Bunsen burner if necessary. Use a regular thermometer to monitor the temperature of the water bath. The test tubes should equilibrate in the boiling water for about five to ten minutes, before used in further experiments.

6.3.3 Determination of the heat capacity of the calorimeter

i) Remove the Styrofoam cup from the 600 mL beaker. Weigh the Styrofoam cup of your calorimeter to the nearest 0.1g. Add about 70 mL of water to the Styrofoam cup, reweigh, and record the mass of the cup plus water. Re-insert the filled Styrofoam cup into the 600 mL beaker.

ii) Lower the temperature probe of the accumet® instrument into the Styrofoam cup. Record the temperature of the water in the Styrofoam cup ($T_{i,cw}$).

iii) Turn to the 600 mL beaker that contains the four test tubes with samples of water and metal. Determine the temperature of the boiling water, and record the temperature in your notebook (T_{hw}).

iv) *Wear an insulated glove*, and quickly but carefully transfer a 30 mL sample of hot water to the Styrofoam cup. Be careful that no hot water from the outside of the test tube drips into the cup. Gently swirl the contents of the Styrofoam cup. Monitor the temperature in the calorimeter. You will see a rise in temperature, and the temperature will remain constant for some time before it begins to drop. In your notebook, record the highest temperature attained as final temperature T_f.

v) Raise the temperature probe out of the cup. Remove the cup from the 600 mL beaker. Reweigh and record the mass of the cup plus water. The mass of the hot water added is the difference between this mass and the mass of the cup plus 70 mL of water.

vi) Pour the water out and dry the inside of the calorimeter.

vii) Repeat the procedure for the second 30 mL hot water sample.

6.3.4 Determination of the specific heat of a metal

i) Reweigh the dry Styrofoam cup to the nearest 0.1 g. Record the mass. Add 70 mL of water to the cup, reweigh, and record the mass of the cups plus water. Re-insert the cup into the 600 mL beaker.

ii) Lower the temperature probe of the accumet® instrument into the Styrofoam cup. Record the temperature of the water in the Styrofoam cup ($T_{i,wc}$).

iii) Turn to the 600 mL beaker that still contains the two test tubes with samples of metal. Determine the temperature of the boiling water, and record the temperature in your notebook ($T_{i,m}$).

iv) *Wear an insulated glove*, and quickly and carefully transfer the first sample of hot metal to the Styrofoam cup. Be careful that no hot water from the outside of the test tube drips into the cups, and that no water is splashing out of the calorimeter. Gently swirl the contents of the Styrofoam cup. Monitor the temperature in the calorimeter. You will see a rise in temperature, and the temperature will remain constant for some time before it begins to drop. In your notebook, record the highest temperature attained as final temperature T_f.

v) Raise the temperature probe out of the cups. Reweigh and record the mass of the cups plus water plus metal. The mass of the metal added is the difference between this mass and the mass of the cups plus 70 mL of water.

vi) Pour the water out, dry the inside of the calorimeter, collect the metal on a piece of paper towel.

vii) Repeat the procedure for the second sample of hot metal.

6.4 Calculations

Determine the heat capacity of the calorimeter for the two trials performed. Calculate the average heat capacity. Using the average heat capacity of the calorimeter, calculate the specific heat of your metal. Average the results of the two metal samples.

Compare your calculated specific heat of the metal to data from table 6-1, and suggest what your metal could be.

6.5 Discussion

State your results. In your discussion, explain how the following errors would affect the results of the experiment:

- The Styrofoam cups were not dry when you determined the mass of the empty cups.

- When the metal was added to the calorimeter, some of the water splashed out.

- When the metal was added to the calorimeter, several of the hot metal beads spilled onto the counter.

- Water splashed into the test tube of metal beads before the beads were weighed.

EXPERIMENT 7: Acid-Base Chemistry II — Strength of an Antacid

7.1 Purpose

In experiment 7, the strength of an antacid will be determined by acid-base titration.

7.2 Background

The stomach contains hydrochloric acid HCl to help activate digestive enzymes and aid in the breakdown of food. Acid indigestion occurs when too much hydrochloric acid is produced. A simple remedy for this is to neutralize the excess acid with a base. Commercial antacids contain a base such as calcium carbonate or magnesium hydroxide for this purpose. For example, magnesium hydroxide, the active component in milk of magnesia, neutralizes HCl in the following reaction, equation 7.1:

$$2\ HCl\ (aq) + Mg(OH)_2(aq) \rightarrow MgCl_2(aq) + 2\ H_2O(l) \tag{7.1}$$

The strength of an antacid tablet is a measure of how much hydrochloric acid it can neutralize.

In order to understand how the strength of an antacid tablet is measured, and how these experiments are carried out, we review a few basic principles of acid-base chemistry and in particular of neutralization reactions.

7.2.1 The concept of equivalent

In general terms, one **equivalent** *eq* of a compound delivers one mole of the *active* species or *active* agent. It is important to note that an equivalent refers to a number of moles. The *active* species is identified in the context of a particular chemical reaction. For example, in acid-base chemistry, the active species are H^+ and OH^-. In redox chemistry, the equivalent is based on the number of electrons that appear in the half-reactions for oxidation and reduction.

Acid-base neutralization reactions are often analyzed in terms of equivalents. One equivalent of an acid is the amount of acid that supplies one mole of H^+ in the neutralization reaction. Not all bases contain OH^- groups (although every base will produce OH^- in aqueous solution). For that reason, one equivalent of a base is defined as the amount of base that neutralizes one mol of H^+. Within these definitions, one equivalent of an acid reacts with one equivalent of a base in any neutralization reaction.

It is helpful to write a neutralization reaction as net-ionic equation:

$$H^+(aq) + OH^-(aq) \rightarrow H_2O(l) \tag{7.2}$$

From equation 7.2, we see that in any neutralization reaction, an equal amount of H^+ reacts with an equal amount of OH^-. The chemical composition of antacids can be quite complex, and their efficiency is therefore best expressed in terms of equivalents. This directly answers the question "How many moles of extra stomach acid can be neutralized by one antacid tablet?"

The **equivalence factor** *feq* converts number of moles *n* into equivalents *eq*.

$$eq = f_{eq} \times n \qquad (7.3)$$

If for example one mole of a base neutralizes two moles of H^+, the **equivalence factor** f_{eq} for that particular base would be two. Equivalence factors for typical acids and bases are given in Table 7-1.

Table 7-1 Equivalence factors for various acids and bases

	Name	**Formula**	f_{eq}
Acid	hydrochloric acid	HCl	1
Acid	Acetic acid	CH_3COOH	1
Acid	sulfuric acid	H_2SO_4	2
Acid	nitric acid	HNO_3	1
Base	sodium hydroxide	Na(OH)	1
Base	magnesium hydroxide	$Mg(OH)_2$	2
Base	sodium carbonate	Na_2CO_3	2
Base	Ammonia	NH_3	1

For an acid, the equivalence factor tells us how many moles of H^+ are delivered by one mole of acid. Similarly, for a base, the equivalence factor tells us how many moles of OH^- are effectively delivered by one mole of base.

7.2.2 Molarity and Normality

Molarity *M* is a concentration unit, concentration being defined as the number of moles per volume of solution:

$$M = n/V \qquad (7.4)$$

The units for M are usually given in mol/L.

Normality *N* is a concentration unit that has a definition similar to molarity *M*. The normality of an acid or base solution is the amount of equivalents per liter of solution.

$$N = eq/V \qquad (7.5)$$

Using equivalence factors f_{eq}, we obtain the following relationship between molarity and normality:

$$N = eq/V = f_{eq} \times n/V = f_{eq} \times M \qquad (7.6)$$

Thus, the normality of a solution of an acid or of a base is obtained by multiplying its molarity (concentration) by its equivalence factor.

7.2.3 Acid-base titration

The purpose of an acid-base titration experiment is to determine either an unknown amount of acid or base in a sample. For example, in the titration of an acid of unknown concentration by a base, the concentration of the acid is determined by carefully adding a measured volume of base of known concentration until the reaction of acid and base is complete. When just enough base has been added to neutralize all of the acid, it is said that the **equivalence point** has been reached. At the equivalence point, the number of equivalents of acid initially present equals the number of equivalents of base added.

Recall that each neutralization reaction is described by equation 7.2, a one-to-one relationship between and OH⁻. Thus, at the end of a neutralization reaction, the number of moles OH⁻ added equals the number of moles of H⁺ initially present.

The number of moles of active species of acid n_{H^+} equals the number of active species of base n_{OH^-}. Using concentration and volume of acid and base, the following relationships can be derived, equation 7.7:

$$eq_{H^+} = eq_{OH^-}$$
$$f_{eq_{acid}} \cdot n_{acid} = f_{eq_{base}} \cdot n_{base}$$
$$f_{eq_{acid}} \cdot c_{acid} \cdot V_{acid} = f_{eq_{base}} \cdot c_{base} \cdot V_{base}$$

$$(7.7)$$

In equation 7.7, V_{acid} is the original volume of the acid sample and V_{base} is the volume of base added. Equation 7.7 can also be expressed in terms of molarity M and normality N, equation 7.8:

$$N_{acid} \cdot V_{acid} = N_{base} \cdot V_{base}$$
$$f_{eq_{acid}} \cdot M_{acid} \cdot V_{acid} = f_{eq_{base}} \cdot M_{base} \cdot V_{base}$$

$$(7.8)$$

A titration makes use of a specialized piece of glassware called a buret. A buret is a glass tube that accurately measures the volume of solution that is dispensed. Further, an **indicator** is added to the acid solution. An indicator is an organic dye that changes color when the **endpoint** of a titration is reached. If the indicator is properly chosen, then the endpoint of the indicator will coincide with the equivalence point of the titration. An appropriate indicator is added to the analyte solution at the beginning of the titration, and the equivalence point is signaled by a change in the color of the solution.

7.2.4 Titrating an antacid

To determine the neutralizing strength of an antacid, one could in principle titrate a solution of the antacid with an acid. However, antacid are commonly not very soluble. To circumvent this problem, an antacid tablet is dissolved in a known amount of excess hydrochloric acid. The antacid neutralizes some of the HCl. The amount of HCl added in excess is determined by titration of the solution with sodium hydroxide, equation 7.9:

$$HCl(aq) + NaOH(aq) \rightarrow NaCl(aq) + H_2O(l)$$

$$(7.9)$$

The amount of HCl neutralized by the antacid tablet is the difference between the amount of HCl that was added to the tablet originally and the amount of HCl that was found to be in excess.

7.2.5 Errors in Titration

There are several common sources of error in a titration. The largest source of error in this experiment is *over-titration*.

An indicator that changes color in the acidic region at pH≈3.5 is bromophenol blue. This indicator is often used when a weak base is titrated with a strong acid. It is blue in basic solutions at the beginning of the titration, and yellow in more acidic solutions. The endpoint of a titration monitored with bromophenol blue is thus reached when the solution takes on a murky green color. It is helpful to place a piece of white paper beneath the flask to help discern this subtle color change. The green end point color will be appear temporarily during the titration, when the titrant first comes into contact with the solution. As the end point is neared, these temporary changes in color will persist for longer amounts of time. At this stage fractional drops of the titrant should be added. It is also good practice at this point to rinse the tip of the buret and the inside of the flask with distilled water to ensure that all of the titrant has made it into the solution. This is especially important when the titrant splatters as it hits the solution. Titrate until the bromophenol blue just begins to change from blue to green. Further addition of titrant will turn the solution yellow. A yellow solution indicates *over-titration*. Operate the stopcock with one hand while swirling the flask with the other throughout the course of all of titrations.

An indicator that changes color in the basic region at pH≈8.5 is phenolphtalein. This indicator is often used when an acid is titrated with a strong base. It is colorless in acidic solutions at the beginning of the titration, and pink in more basic solutions. The endpoint of a titration monitored with phenolphtalein is thus reached when the solution takes on slight pink color. It is helpful to place a piece of white paper beneath the flask to discern this subtle color change. During the titration there will be a temporary appearance of a pink color when the titrant first comes into contact with the solution. As the end point is neared, these temporary changes in color will persist for longer amounts of time. At this stage fractional drops of the titrant should be added. It is also good practice at this point to rinse the tip of the buret and the inside of the flask with distilled water to ensure that all of the titrant has made it into the solution. This is especially important when the titrant splatters as it hits the solution. The most accurate end point is signaled when the solution from colorless to the faintest intensity of pink discernible. A bright pink solution has been over-titrated, and the titration must be repeated.

Another source of error is an incorrect reading of the volume of titrant. Read the volume at the bottom of the meniscus, with the meniscus at eye level. A piece of paper placed behind the buret will make it easier to read.

7.2.6 Standardization of acid-base solutions

The analysis requires the concentrations of the HCl and NaOH solutions used in the procedure to be known very accurately. The standardization of these two solutions is done by titration. The HCl is standardized first and is then used to standardize the NaOH.

The concentration of HCl is determined by titration with sodium carbonate Na_2CO_3, equation 7.10:

$$Na_2CO_3(aq) + 2\ HCl(aq) \rightarrow NaCl(aq) + CO_2\ (g) + H_2O(l) \qquad \textbf{(7.10)}$$

We keep in mind that the equivalence factor of sodium carbonate is 2.

An accurately measured mass of sodium carbonate is dissolved in water, and the solution is titrated with the hydrochloric acid of unknown concentration. The number of moles of Na_2CO_3 in the sample is obtained by dividing the mass of Na_2CO_3 by its molar mass or molecular weight, equation 7.11:

$$n_{Na_2CO_3} = \frac{m_{Na_2CO_3}}{MW_{Na_2CO_3}} = \frac{m_{Na_2CO_3}}{106.00\ g/mol}$$

$$\textbf{(7.11)}$$

From the number of moles of sodium carbonate, and from the volume of water in which sodium carbonate was dissolved, the concentration of sodium carbonate is obtained. The Molarity and Normality of the HCl solution can then be calculated according to equations 7.4 and 7.6.

Once the HCl solution has been standardized, it can be used to determine the concentration of the sodium hydroxide solution.

7.3 Procedure

Set up the following table in your notebook in which you collect your results:

HCl-Standard	Sample #1	Sample #2	Sample #3
m(Na_2CO_3) (g)			
buret intial (mL)			
buret final (mL)			
NaOH-Standard	Sample #1	Sample #2	Sample #3
V(HCl) (mL)	25 mL	25 mL	25 mL
buret intial (mL)			
buret final (mL)			
Antacid	Sample #1	Sample #2	
V(HCl) (mL)	25 mL	25 mL	
buret intial (mL)			
buret final (mL)			

The experiment might be carried out by two students, or two groups of students. The first student prepares and standardizes the HCl Solution, while the second student prepares and standardizes the NaOH solution. Both groups share not only data, but also their standardized solution. Since you will prepare solutions used by other students, be especially careful when you prepare and analyze the standards. Each group will analyze one or two antacid tablets of the same brand, and share their results.

Detailed step by step procedures for the different titrations are given below.

7.3.1 Standardization of Hydrochloric Acid:

i) Fill a 500 mL polyethylene bottle about half full with de-ionized water.

ii) *In the hood*, pour 30 mL of *concentrated hydrochloric acid* into the water. Fill the bottle to its neck with de-ionized water and mix. Properly label the polyethylene bottle. The resulting hydrochloric acid solution is approximately 0.7 N.

iii) Obtain three 250 mL Erlenmeyer flasks. Properly label the Erlenmeyer flasks, *e.g.* sample 1, sample 2, sample 3.

iv) Weigh out about 0.6 g of Na_2CO_3 on a piece of weighing paper. Record the mass of the sample to the nearest 0.001 g. Do not include the mass of the weighing paper (weighing by difference). Add the sample of sodium carbonate to the first Erlenmeyer flask. Repeat this procedure for the remaining two Erlenmeyer flasks.

v) Add about 100 mL of de-ionized water to each Erlenmeyer flask. Add 5 drops of bromophenol blue to each sample. Mix the samples thoroughly by gently swirling the flasks.

vi) Rinse a buret several times with de-ionized water and then with about 5 mL of your HCl solution. Make sure that the entire inner surface of the buret and the tip of the buret come into contact with the solution.

vii) Fill the buret with the HCl solution. Drain a small amount of solution to remove any air bubbles in the buret.

viii) Read the buret to the nearest 0.05 mL (initial reading).

ix) Slowly add HCl solution to one of the sodium carbonate samples. Swirl the flask continuously while you titrate. Take the appropriate measures as the end point approaches: add single drops or fractions of a drop, rinse the tip of the buret and the inside of the flask with de-ionized water. When the color change persists for more than a minute, the end point has been reached.

x) Record the volume of the HCl solution in the buret to the nearest 0.05 mL (final reading).

xi) Repeat steps *viii* to *x* for the remaining two samples.

7.3.2 Standardization of Aqueous Sodium Hydroxide

i) Weigh about 15.0 g of solid sodium hydroxide to the nearest 0.001g, and place the sample in a 500 mL polyethylene bottle. Properly label the polyethylene bottle.

ii) Fill the bottle half full with de-ionized water and mix until the NaOH is completely dissolved.

iii) Fill the bottle to the neck with de-ionized water and mix. The resulting sodium hydroxide solution is approximately 0.75 N.

iv) Drain the buret, and rinse it several times with de-ionized water. Then rinse the buret with about 5 mL of the NaOH solution. Make sure that the entire inner surface of the buret and its tip come into contact with the solution.

v) Fill the buret with the NaOH solution. Check for air bubbles in the buret. Read the volume to the nearest 0.05 mL.

vi) Rinse a clean 25-mL pipet with distilled water. Discard the rinse water and repeat two more times.

vii) Rinse the pipet with a few mL of the standardized HCl solution. Make sure that the HCl solution comes into contact with the entire inner surface of the pipet. Discard the rinse solution and repeat.

viii) Carefully pipet 25.0 mL of the HCl solution into a 250-mL Erlenmeyer flask. Rinse the inside surface of the flask with de-ionized water. Add about 50 mL of de-ionized water. Repeat this step to prepare a total of three HCl solutions for titration. Add 3 drops phenolphthalein to each HCl sample.

ix) Carefully titrate each HCl sample with NaOH to its phenolphthalein end point. Be careful to record the initial and final volumes for each titration.

7.3.3 Determination of the Strength of an Antacid Tablet

i) Place an antacid tablet in a 250-mL beaker. Record the brand name of your tablet in your notebook. Add 25.0 mL of the standardized HCl solution by using an appropriately rinsed pipet. Mix the solution well with a glass stirring rod to make sure that all of the antacid tablet dissolves, and rinse the stirring rod off into the solution with de-ionized water.

ii) Add 3 drops of phenolphthalein to the solution.

iii) Fill the buret with the standardized NaOH solution and record the initial volume. Carefully titrate the contents of the beaker to the phenolphthalein end point. Record the final volume.

iv) Repeat the analysis for a second time.

iv) When all titrations have been completed, drain the buret and rinse it three times with distilled water. Thoroughly clean all other glassware.

7.4 Calculations

Set up the following table in your notebook in which you summarize your calculaions:

HCl-Standard	Sample #1	Sample #2	Sample #3	Average
$n(Na_2CO_3)$ (mol)				
$eq(Na_2CO_3)$ (mol)				
M(HCl) (mol/L)				
N(HCl) (mol/L)				
NaOH-Standard	Sample #1	Sample #2	Sample #3	Average
n(HCl) (mol)				
eq(HCl) (mol)				
M(NaOH) (mol/L)				
N(NaOH) (mol/L)				
Antacid	Sample #1	Sample #2	Average	
n(HCl) remaining(mol)				
n(HCl) reacted(mol)				
eq(HCl) reacted(mol)				
eq(base) antacid(mol)				

7.4.1 Standardization of Hydrochloric Acid

In your report, include one sample calculation in which you show in detail how to obtain equivalents, molarity, and normality. Perform these calculations for all trials.

i) Calculate the number of equivalents of Na_2CO_3 in each of the three samples that were titrated.

ii) Calculate the normality of the HCl solution from the number of equivalents of HCl neutralized and the volume of HCl solution required for the titration.

iii) Determine the average normality of the HCl standard solution.

7.4.2 Standardization of Aqueous Sodium Hydroxide

Use the average normality of HCl calculated in section 7.4.1. In your report, include one sample calculation in which you show in detail how to obtain equivalents, molarity, and normality. Perform these calculations for all trials.

i) Calculate the normality of the NaOH solution for each trial by using the average normality of the standardized HCl solution.

ii) Determine the average normality of the NaOH standard solution.

7.4.3 Determination of the Strength of an Antacid Tablet

Use the average normalities of HCl and NaOH calculated in sections 7.4.1 and 7.4.2. In your report, include one sample calculation in which you show in detail how to obtain equivalents, molarity, and normality. Perform these calculations for all trials.

i) Calculate the number of equivalents of excess HCl neutralized by sodium hydroxide, by using the average normality of your NaOH standard solution.

ii) Determine the total number of equivalents of acid used to dissolve the antacid tablet.

iii) Determine the number of equivalents of base in the antacid tablet.

7.5 Discussion

State your results. Remember to include the brand and strength of the antacid used.

Explain why you used a back titration to determine the strength of the antacid tablet. Consider the questions related to the following alternate procedure when formulating your explanation:

An alternate method of determining the strength of the antacid is to directly titrate the antacid with HCl. The disadvantage of using this method is that the reaction between the antacid is slow because the antacid is a solid, and it is not very soluble in water. Why would the slow reaction be a problem for a direct titration? Would a slow acid-base reaction make finding the endpoint more or less difficult? How does the back titration get around the problem of the slow acid neutralization by the antacid tablet?

EXPERIMENT 8: The Ideal Gas Law —
Molar Mass of a Volatile Liquid

8.1 Purpose

In experiment 8, the molar mass of an unknown volatile liquid will be determined by using an application of the ideal gas law.

8.2 Background

Chemical and physical methods of determining atomic and molecular formula weights or molar masses have been important historically as a way of analyzing and categorizing new materials. The modern laboratory is generally equipped with instrumentation which makes many of these methods obsolete. However, the principles upon which the older methods were based are not insignificant, and many form the foundation for the prediction of physical and chemical properties and behaviors of substances.

The classic *Dumas Method* for determining the formula weight of a volatile liquid is a case in point. As early as the mid-1800's Avogadro proposed that equal volumes of gases measured under identical conditions would contain equal numbers of gas particles. At standard pressure and temperature, this volume is 22.4 L for an ideal gas.

An understanding of the ideal gas law allows us to apply this useful information to liquids which are appreciably volatile. As long as temperature and pressure are known, a measured volume of gas can be converted to moles. Assuming the gas behaves ideally, the number of moles of gas is given by

$$n = \frac{P \cdot V}{R \cdot T}$$

(8.1)

In equation 8.1, P is the pressure and T is the temperature (in Kelvin) of a sample of gas of volume V. R is the ideal gas constant. The ideal gas constant has a value of 0.08206 L·atm·mol^{-1}·K^{-1} if pressure is in atmospheres and volume is in liters.

Massing a sample of gas is relatively simple, and these two pieces of information are the minimum requirements for a molar mass determination.

The molar mass M of a gas is equal to the mass of a given amount of gas m divided by the number of moles n:

$$M = \frac{m}{n}$$

(8.2)

If we combine equations 8.1 and 8.2, we get the following expression for the molar mass of a gas:

$$M = \frac{m \cdot R \cdot T}{P \cdot V}$$

(8.3)

Equation 8.3 can be rewritten in terms of density d of the gas, equation 8.4:

$$M = d \cdot \frac{R \cdot T}{P}$$

(8.4)

In the *Dumas Method*, a volatile liquid is heated to a known temperature above its boiling point, and allowed to escape from a container through a tiny orifice. Once the liquid has vaporized, the container is cooled to room temperature. Gradually the vapor which remained in the container at the higher temperature condenses to a liquid and is then massed. As long as the volume of the container is known along with the high temperature, the atmospheric pressure can be used to calculate moles. This approach is justified since the system is open to the atmosphere through the orifice. From there a molar mass can be determined.

The success of this method depends on a lot of things going right. One assumption is that while the liquid is volatile enough to vaporize at the elevated temperature, it is not so volatile that a significant amount will be lost to evaporation through the orifice as the container cools. The vapor is assumed to behave ideally at the temperature and pressure at which it occupies the container. It is further assumed that the vapor has reached thermal equilibrium with the hot water bath. If any of these assumptions are not met, errors in the molecular weight determination may occur — the molecular weight is either too low or too high. Nevertheless, the Dumas methods yields good first approximations within a few g/mol for the molecular weight of a volatile liquid.

In this experiment, a sample of the unknown volatile liquid is placed in a weighed Dumas flask. The liquid is heated to a temperature above its boiling point, causing it to vaporize. The vapor produced drives the air out of the flask through the orifice. Excess compound also escapes, leaving the flask filled with vapor at atmospheric pressure. The flask is then cooled to room temperature and the vapor condenses. The flask and its contents are weighed again to determine the mass of the liquid that filled the flask in vapor form.

8.3 Procedure

The liquids used in this experiment are flammable. *Perform the experiment in a hood.* Keep the liquids well removed from open flames. Dispose of your samples in the appropriate waste container. *You also need to record the atmospheric pressure.*

i) A clean, dry 125 mL Erlenmeyer flask makes a suitable container for the construction of a Dumas flask. A cap is fashioned for the flask from a square of aluminum foil (about 3cm × 3cm) and secured with fine copper wire twisted tightly around the neck just below the rim.

ii) Determine the mass of the assembled flask to the nearest 0.001 g.

iii) Fill a 600mL beaker with 400-450mL of water. Place the filled beaker on a wire gauze on a ring stand. Adjust the height so that the beaker can be heated with a Bunsen burner. Clamp the neck of the 125-mL flask to the ring stand and immerse it into the water, Figure 8-1. Make sure that the water does not touch the aluminum foil.

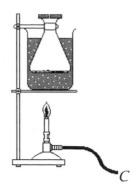

Figure 8-1: Experimental set-up for the Dumas experiment

The water level should be high enough to cover most of the flask but not so high as to allow water to bubble in around and under the copper wire loop. If necessary, add or remove water to or from the 600mL beaker.

  iv) Heat the water to boil. The water should boil only gently, since rising bubbles of water vapor obstruct the observation of the contents of the flask. If the water is boiling violently, remove the Bunsen burner. Monitor the temperature with a thermometer; when the temperature drops below the boiling point of water, replace the Bunsen burner and continue heating. It is also of important that the Dumas flask be submerged during the process of heating. This ensures that a thermal equilibrium between the water bath and the contents of the flask will be readily established.

  v) With a syringe or with a Pasteur pipette, introduce about 3 mL of an unknown volatile liquid into the Dumas flask. The needle is used to make a tiny hole in the foil cap, which also serves as orifice for the excess vapor the escape.

  vi) Continue to heat the Dumas flask to the point when all liquid has evaporated and thermal equilibrium between water bath and vapor is achieved. Once the liquid has been injected, you can see it boil inside the Dumas flask.

If your unknown is of moderate molecular weight, you will also observe that the vapor will condense in the upper region of the flask, and that drops of condensed liquid are running down to the bottom of the flask. Initially, you can clearly see the phase boundary between the liquid and the vapor. When the point of complete vaporization has been reached, the phase boundary disappears, and no more condensation droplets are observed. Keep the flask in the hot water bath for a few more minutes, and then remove it. Record the temperature of the water bath at the time when the flask is removed.

If your unknown is of low molecular weight the escaping vapor can be be monitored by the presence of *Schlieren Jets*, which are best observed against a piece of white paper. They look like a jet engine exhaust or a swirling cloud, Figure 8-2.

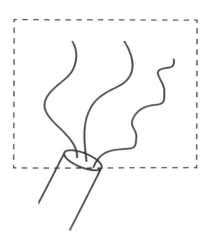

Figure 8-2: Schlieren Jets

Once the Schlieren Jets can no longer be observed, the gas has reached thermal equilibrium with its surroundings. If the Dumas flask is properly preheated, it should take no more than two minutes after injection of the unknown to completely vaporize and occupy the interior of the Dumas flask. Remove the flask and record the temperature of the water bath at the time the flask is removed.

vii) Cool the flask to room temperature. Run cold water over the flask to aid the cooling process. Water must be removed completely from the outside of the flask. Be especially careful about the cap edges as steam from the boiling water can condense just under the edges and change the mass of the container significantly. When the flask has returned to room temperature and is completely dry, record the mass of the flask, cover and condensed liquid to the nearest mg.

vii) Repeat the procedure with a second sample of the same unknown. Use the same flask, and do not empty out its contents. Immerse the Dumas flask into the water bath, and reheat. Once the water boils, add another 1-2mL of the same unknown liquid to the flask through the same hole. Repeat the procedure described above.

viii) After you are finished with all determinations, rinse the flask with acetone, and then with water, to remove all remnants of the volatile liquid. To determine the volume of the Erlenmeyer flask, add a measured amount of water to the flask until it is completely full. Use a 100mL graduated cylinder and add exactly 140 mL of water to the flask. Then use a 10mL graduated cylinder and add enough water to completely fill the flask.

8.4 Calculations

Determine the molar mass of your unknown for the two trials performed, and average your results.

8.5 Discussion

State your results and discuss errors you may have incurred. In your discussion explain how the following errors would affect the results for the molar mass:

• The flask containing condensed liquid was not dried before the final weighing.

• All of the liquid had vaporized, but the vapor had not yet come to thermal equilibrium with the boiling water when the flask was removed from the water and cooled.

EXPERIMENT 9: Thermochemistry II — Reaction Enthalpies

9.1 Purpose

In experiment 9, the enthalpy of reaction ΔH for two acid-base reactions and their component reactions will be determined, employing and confirming Hess' law.

9.2 Background

The idea of **enthalpy H** in its use and definition is one of the most powerful concepts in **thermochemistry**. It allows us to calculate heat of reactions from a small number of measurements for a multitude of chemical processes. An important notion here is that enthalpy H is a **state function**. A state function is one whose change is independent of the pathway by which a chemical reaction occurs. Further, the *change in enthalpy ΔH*, which is directly related to heats of reaction ΔH^0_{rxn}, is an **extensive** property and *changes sign* when a process is reversed. These basic ideas are the foundation for **Hess' Law of Constant Heat Summation**, which states:

> *When a process occurs in stages or steps, or is considered to occur in stages or steps, the enthalpy change for the overall process is the sum of the enthalpy changes for the individual steps.*

Here, it is irrelevant whether the chemical reaction does, or even can, occur by the series of steps proposed for a calculation of its overall enthalpy change. Hess' law allows one to determine the change in enthalpy associated with a chemical reaction for which this change can be measured only with difficulty, if at all. In general terms, *Hess' Law* can be formulated as shown in equation 9.0:

$$\Delta H^0_{rxn} = a \cdot \Delta H^0_A + b \cdot \Delta H^0_B + c \cdot \Delta H^0_C + ... \tag{9.0}$$

In equation 9.0, A, B, C,⋯ refer to the balanced thermochemical equations of each reaction that can be summed to give the equation for the desired overall chemical reaction. The underlying concept of Hess' law is also referred to as **additivity of enthalpies of reaction**.

9.2.1 Reaction of solid sodium hdroxide with acids

A useful known application of Hess' law is the prediction of enthalpies of acid-base neutralization reactions in cases where one of the reaction partners is not employed as aqueous solution. This type of reaction is for example illustrated in the reaction between solid sodium hydroxide $NaOH(s)$ and an aqueous solution of an acid HX. The acid might either be a strong acid such as hydrochloric acid HCl, or a weak acid such as acetic acid CH_3COOH, for short AcOH. The **net ionic equation** for this reaction, referred to as reaction 1, is illustrated in equation 9.1:

$$rxn1: NaOH(s) + H^+(aq) \rightarrow Na^+(aq) + H_2O(l) \quad \Delta H^0_{rxn1} \tag{9.1}$$

Data that are readily available are heats of solution, here the heat of solution of sodium hydroxide — reaction 2 — and heats of neutralization in aqueous solution, here the acid-base reaction of an aqueous solution of the strong base sodium hydroxide with an aqueous solution of the acid HX — reaction 3. Net ionic equations for reactions 2 and 3 are given in equations 9.2 and 9.3, respectively:

$$rxn2: NaOH(s) + H_2O(l) \rightarrow Na^+(aq) + OH^-(aq) \quad \Delta H^0_{rxn2} \tag{9.2}$$

$$rxn3: OH^-(aq) + H^+(aq) \rightarrow H_2O(l) \quad\quad\quad \Delta H^0_{rxn3} \tag{9.3}$$

After examining the three reactions illustrated in equations 9.1 to 9.3, it is evident that the target reaction 1 is the sum of reactions 2 and 3. Therefore, in agreement with Hess' law, we get the following expression for the enthalpy of the target reaction 1 (equation 9.4):

$$\Delta H^0_{rxn1} = \Delta H^0_{rxn2} + \Delta H^0_{rxn3} \tag{9.4}$$

The above net ionic equations suggest that the heat of the reaction between solid sodium hydroxide and an aqueous solution of an acid is independent of the nature of the acid. Whether you treat solid sodium hydroxide with an aqueous solution of hydrochloric acid or an aqueous solution of acetic acid, you can expect to get the same change in enthalpy for both neutralization reactions.

Enthalpies of reactions can also be obtained from **standard enthalpies of formation** ΔH^0_f of reactants and products. The *standard enthalpy of formation* of a substance is the *enthalpy change* that occurs in the formation of one mol of a substance in its standard state from the reference form of its elements in their standard state. The standard enthalpy of formation of elements is zero, and the following expression holds for the enthalpy of a reaction (equation 9.5):

$$\Delta H^0_{rxn} = \sum \nu_p \Delta H^0_f(prod.) - \sum \nu_r \Delta H^0_f(react.) \tag{9.5}$$

In equation 9.5, ν_p and ν_r represent the stoichiometric coefficients with which products and reactants enter the reaction equation.

By employing the relation of equation 9.5, you can calculate the enthalpy of the target reaction 1 ΔH^0_{rxn1} as follows (equation 9.6):

$$\Delta H^0_{rxn} = \left\{ \Delta H^0_f[H_2O(l)] + \Delta H^0_f[Na^+(aq)] \right\}$$
$$- \left\{ \Delta H^0_f[NaOH(s)] + \Delta H^0_f[H^+(aq)] \right\} \tag{9.6}$$

If one chooses to formulate the target reaction 1, the reaction of solid sodium hydroxide NaOH(s) with an aqueous solution of an acid HX (X⁻ = Cl⁻ or AcO⁻), not as *net ionic equation* but as *full ionic equation* with inclusion of the *spectator* species, the following reaction equation is obtained (equation 9.7):

$$rxn1: NaOH(s) + H^+(aq) + X^-(aq) \rightarrow Na^+(aq) + H_2O(l) + X^-(aq) \tag{9.7}$$

Using the relation given in equation 9.5, an expression is obtained for the enthalpy of the target reaction 1 (equation 9.8):

$$\Delta H^0_{rxn} = \left\{ \Delta H^0_f[H_2O(l)] + \Delta H^0_f[Na^+(aq)] + \Delta H^0_f[X^-(aq)] \right\}$$
$$- \left\{ \Delta H^0_f[NaOH(s)] + \Delta H^0_f[H^+(aq)] + \Delta H^0_f[X^-(aq)] \right\} \tag{9.8}$$

In equation 9.8, the standard heat of formation of the anion X⁻ in aqueous solution will cancel out, and equation 9.8 can be simplified to yield the previously obtained expression, equation 9.6. This treatment for the heat of the target reaction 1 again illustrates the fact that the heat of neutralization of solid sodium hydroxide with an aqueous solution of an acid is independent of the nature of the acid, be it a strong acid or a weak acid.

9.2.2 Calorimetric measurements

Heats of reactions are conveniently measured with a device called a **calorimeter**. Numerous types of calorimeters exist, each suitable for a specific type of reaction. A chemical reaction is performed within a calorimeter, and the heat gained by the calorimeter set-up $q_{calorim}$ is measured by a change in temperature ΔT:

$$q_{calorim} = C_{calorim} \cdot \Delta T \qquad (9.9)$$

A simple type of calorimeter that is suitable for measuring heats of reaction in aqueous solution is the so called *Styrofoam-cup calorimeter*. This term simply refers to a thermally insulated reaction vessel in which a chemical reaction is carried out, such as a Styrofoam cup.

The heat produced in a chemical reaction that takes place within the calorimeter is absorbed by the solution contained in the calorimeter and by the Styrofoam cup of the calorimeter itself. Thus, $q_{calorim}$ can be partitioned into two components:

$$q_{calorim} = q_{solution} + q_{cup} \qquad (9.10)$$

Here, q_{cup} is the heat absorbed by the Styrofoam cup, compare experiment 6. This value is generally small, but no negligible. We can also express equation 9.10 in terms of heat capacities and temperature changes:

$$q_{calorim} = (C_{solution} + C_{cup}) \cdot \Delta T \qquad (9.11)$$

In equation 9.9, C_{cup} is the *heat capacity* of the Styrofoam cup of the calorimeter set-up. Further, the heat gained by the calorimeter is directly related to the heat produced by the chemical reaction:

$$q_{calorim} = -q_{rxn} \qquad (9.12)$$

In order to obtain a sensible value for $q_{calorim}$ the following simplifying assumptions are made: i) the heat loss to the surroundings is negligible. ii) the relevant properties of the aqueous solution, such as its heat capacity, its density and its volume, are equal to the properties of the solvent, in this case water. Therefore, we get for the heat of the calorimeter the following expression:

$$q_{calorim} = (C_{H_2O} + C_{cup}) \cdot \Delta T$$

$$q_{calorim} = (m_{H_2O} \cdot c_{H_2O} + C_{cup}) \, \Delta T \qquad (9.13)$$

$$q_{calorim} = (V_{H_2O} \cdot d_{H_2O} \cdot c_{H_2O} + C_{cup}) \, \Delta T$$

In equation 9.13, V_{H_2O} denotes the total volume of solution contained within the calorimeter, d_{H_2O} is the density of water for which we assume a value of 1.00 g/ml, and c_{H_2O} is the specific heat of water, $c_{H_2O} = 4.18 \, J \cdot g^{-1} \cdot °C^{-1}$. With these values, we get for the heat of reaction:

$$q_{rxn} = -(V_{H_2O} \cdot 4.18 J \cdot mL^{-1} \cdot K^{-1} + C_{cup}) \cdot \Delta T \qquad (9.14)$$

As mentioned above, the enthalpy of reaction ΔH^0_{rxn} is an extensive property and is directly proportional to the amounts of substances that undergo a chemical reaction. In order to convert the extensive property into an absolute measurement that is independent of the amount of substances in a system, heats of reactions are commonly reported as energy per amount of substance, with the units J/mol or kJ/mol.

As can be inferred from equations 9.1, 9.3, and 9.7, acid and base components react in an equimolar fashion in the neutralization reaction investigated in this experiment. If both species are present in the same amount of moles, both species are completely consumed during neutralization. If one species is present in a smaller quantity, only this species will be consumed completely, and is referred to as *limiting reagent L.R.* The amount of substance that is consumed during neutralization is therefore equal to the amount of the limiting reagent, $n_{L.R.}$ The enthalpy of reaction is then given as

$$\Delta H_{rxn} = \frac{q_{rxn}}{n_{L.R.}}$$

(9.15)

By combining equations 9.14 and 9.15, we arrive at the following expression for the enthalpy of the neutralization reaction:

$$\Delta H_{rxn} = \frac{-(4.18\,J \cdot mL^{-1} \cdot K^{-1} \cdot V_{H_2O} + C_{cup}) \cdot \Delta T}{n_{L.R.}}$$

(9.16)

When the total volume of solution V_{H_2O}, the change in temperature ΔT (remember that $\Delta T = T_{final} - T_{initial}$), and the amount of limiting reagent $n_{L.R}$ are entered into equation 9.14 with their correct units, the heat of reaction obtained from equation 9.14 will be in units J/mol. This then can easily be converted into kJ/mol. Remember that ΔT yields the same value independent of whether the temperatures are reported in degree Celsius or Kelvin.

9.2.3 One-step and two-step reactions

As we have seen above, the enthalpy of the reaction between solid sodium hydroxide NaOH(s) with an aqueous solution of an acid HX can be determined directly from one reaction only (rxn1), or in a combination of two reactions (rxn2 and rxn3). Using the one-step reaction is referred to as a *direct* measurement, whereas using the two-step reaction is referred to as *indirect* measurement. Both measurements have their advantages and disadvantages. A schematic enthalpy diagram for both types of neutralization reactions is depicted in Figure 9-1.

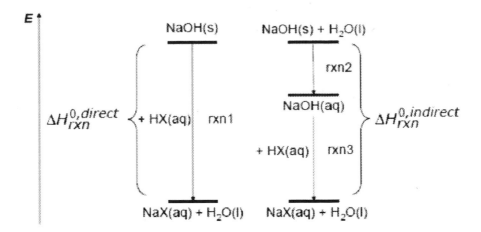

Figure 9-1: Direct (one-step) and indirect (two step) neutralization pathways.

We will utilize direct as well as indirect measurements of the enthalpy of neutralization of solid sodium hydroxide with solutions of an acid (the *target* reaction rxn1, equation 9.1) Ideally, both measurements should result in the same value of ΔH^0_{rxm1}. We will also use two different acidic solutions, one of the strong acid (hydrochloric acid HCl) and one of weak acid (acetic acid, CH_3COOH or AcOH). Again, both acids should result in the same value of ΔH^0_{rxm1}.

9.3 Procedure

In this experiment, we will employ aqueous solutions of HCl, CH_3COOH, and NaOH, as well as solid sodium hydroxide. *Handle the acidic and basic solutions and especially the solid NaOH with care in order to avoid burns.* Since solid sodium hydroxide is *hygroscopic*, be sure to always reclose the NaOH(s) supply bottle after use.

9.3.1 Set-up of the calorimeter:

Temperatures will be measured by using the accumet® AB15 pH/mV/°C Meter. Place a Styrofoam cup into a 600ml beaker, or into a second Styrofoam cup. Arrange the calorimeter and accumet® instrument so that the temperature probe can be conveniently lowered into the Styrofoam cup.

9.3.2 Determination of the heat capacity of the calorimeter

Follow the procedure described in section 6.3.1 and 6.3.3 of experiment 6. When you already have carried out experiment 6, you also might use the value for the heat capacity of the calorimeter that you have determined in experiment 6. Make a proper remark in your lab notebook.

9.3.3 General procedure for a calorimetric experiment:

A procedure for the reaction between an *initial reaction solution* and a *chemical reactant* is described in the following steps.

i) Measure out the *initial reaction solution* into the Styrofoam cup. Lower the Temperature probe into the solution, and monitor the temperature. After a period of about 20 seconds, the temperature probe should be equilibrated and the temperature should be stable. Record this temperature as *initial temperature, T_1*.

ii) Add the *chemical reactant* to the Styrofoam cup. Stir continuously with a stirring rod. The temperature will reach a maximum value, maintain the maximum value for some time, and then begin to drop again due to heat loss to the surroundings. Record the maximum temperature as the *final temperature T_2*.

In your notebook, set-up the following table in which you will collect the results of your measurements. Make sure that you also report the correct units.

	m(NaOH)	V(NaOH)	V(H₂O)	V(acid)	T₁	T₂
NaOH(s) + H₂O		-		-		
NaOH(s) + HCl		-				
NaOH(s) + AcOH		-				
NaOH(aq) + HCl	-					
NaOH(aq) + AcOH	-					

9.3.4 Heat of solution of NaOH(s):

Follow the general procedure outlined in section 9.3.3. Use 100.0 ml de-ionized water as *initial reaction solution*. Solid sodium hydroxide will serve as *chemical reactant*. Weigh out about 2 grams of NaOH(s), and record the mass to the nearest 0.01 g. Since sodium hydroxide is *hygroscopic* and readily absorbs water from the air, it is necessary to weigh it and proceed to the next step without delay.

9.3.5 Reaction of NaOH(s) with a strong acid

Follow the general procedure outlined in section 9.3.3. Use 75.0ml of 1.00M hydrochloric acid HCl and 50.0 ml of de-ionized water as *initial reaction solution*. Solid sodium hydroxide will serve as *chemical reactant*. Weigh out about 2 grams of NaOH(s), and record the mass to the nearest 0.01 g. Since sodium hydroxide is *hygroscopic* and readily absorbs water from the air, it is necessary to weigh it and proceed to the next step without delay.

9.3.6 Reaction of NaOH(s) with a weak acid

Follow the general procedure outlined in section 9.3.3. Use 75.0ml of 1.00M acetic acid CH₃COOH and 50.0 ml of de-ionized water as *initial reaction solution*. Solid sodium hydroxide will serve as *chemical reactant*. Weigh out about 2 grams of NaOH(s), and record the mass to the nearest 0.01g. Since sodium hydroxide is *hygroscopic* and readily absorbs water from the air, it is necessary to weigh it and proceed to the next step without delay.

9.3.7 Neutralization of NaOH(aq) with a strong acid

Follow the general procedure as outlined in section 9.3.3. Use 50.0 ml of 1.00 M hydrochloric acid HCl as *initial reaction solution*, and 50.0 ml of 1.00 M sodium hydroxide NaOH as *chemical reactant*.

9.3.8 Neutralization of NaOH(aq) with a weak acid

Follow the general procedure as outlined in section 9.3.3. Use 50.0 ml of 1.00 M acetic acid CH_3COOH as initial reaction solution, and 50.0 ml of 1.00 M sodium hydroxide NaOH as chemical reactant.

9.4 Calculations

For all reactions you have carried out, calculate the enthalpy of reaction ΔH_{rxn} according to equation 9.16. Calculate the number of moles of sodium hydroxide and of acid. Set up the following table in which your report your results:

	n(NaOH) (mol)	n(acid) (mol)	V_{total} (mL)	ΔT (K or °C)	ΔH^0_{rxn} (kJ/mol)
NaOH(s) + H_2O		–			
NaOH(s) + HCl					
NaOH(s) + AcOH					
NaOH(aq) + HCl					
NaOH(aq) + AcOH					

For each type of calculation (moles of NaOH from solid sodium hydroxide, moles of NaOH from a solution of sodium hydroxide, moles of acid, heat or reaction), include one detailed sample calculation in your report. For each reaction, state the *limiting reagent.*

Use your enthalpies of reaction, and calculate the enthalpy of reaction for the neutralization of solid sodium hydroxide NaOH(s) with acidic solution. We restate the net ionic equation for this reaction:

$$NaOH(s) + H^+(aq) \rightarrow Na^+(aq) + H_2O(l) \qquad \Delta H^0_{neutralization} \qquad \textbf{(9.1)}$$

For both the strong acid and the weak acid, calculate a value for $\Delta H^0_{neutralization}$ following a 1-step and a 2-step process, as outlined in Figure 9-2. Also calculate a theoretical value. You will use equation 9.5 and standard enthalpies of formation listed in Table 9-1. For each measured value, calculate the percent error %E:

$$\%E = \frac{|\text{experimental value - theoretical value}|}{\text{theoretical value}} \times 100\%$$

Table 9-1: Some Standard Enthalpies of formation

SPECIES	$\Delta H^0_{f, 298}$ (kJ/mol)
NaOH(s)	-425.61
$H_2O(l)$	-285.83
$H^+(aq)$	0.00
$Na^+(aq)$	-240.12
$OH^-(aq)$	-229.99
$Cl^-(aq)$	-167.16
$CH_3COO^-(aq)$	-486.01

Set up the following table in which you present your results:

	$\Delta H^0_{neutralization}$	%E
Theory – equation 9.1		
NaOH(s) + HCl: 1-step reaction		
NaOH(s) + HCl: 2-step reaction		
NaOH(s) + AcOH: 1-step reaction		
NaOH(s) + AcOH: 2-step reaction		

9.5 Discussion

State the gist of your results. Comment on possible systematic as well as random errors. Discuss whether your experiment confirms that the enthalpy of the neutralization reaction is independent of the nature of the acid. Discuss which method, the direct (1-step) or the indirect (2-step) procedure, results in values closer to the theoretical value.

EXPERIMENT 10: Absorption Spectrophotometry — Concentration Measurements

10.1 Purpose

In experiment 10, we establish the amount of a reductant in a redox reaction by using absorption spectrophotometry.

10.2 Background

In the fields of physics and in physical chemistry, **spectrophotometry** represents the quantitative study of electromagnetic spectra. In this experiment, we will employ *quantitative measurements* of concentrations of reagents by monitoring the **absorption** of visible light. **Absorption** is the process by which the energy of a photon is taken up by another entity, for example by an atom or molecule whose valence electrons make transitions between two electronic energy levels. The frequencies ν of light absorbed by a molecule or polyatomic ion are related to the energy differences ΔE between allowed quantum states, $\Delta E = h\nu$. Here, we are concerned with the absorption of radiation in the visible region of the electromagnetic spectrum, which causes a valence electron in an atom, a molecule, or polyatomic ion to be promoted to an excited electronic state.

The perceived color of a substance is closely related to its visible absorption spectrum. When a substance absorbs visible light, the color perceived is complementary to the color most strongly absorbed by the sample. In Table 10.1, pairs of complementary colors and the corresponding wavelength ranges are presented.

As an illustrative example, we consider the permanganate ion MnO_4^-. Permanganate is a strong oxidizing agent, and we will measure the change in concentration of permanganate in order to deduce an unknown concentration of a reductant. Permanganate ion in an aqueous solution absorbs visible radiation around 550 nm with an absorption maximum at 525 nm. The visible absorption spectrum of permanganate is displayed in Figure 10-1. Permanganate ion absorbs light of a wavelength corresponding to a green color, and therefore appears as purple colored solution.

Table 10.1 Pairs of absorbed and observed colors for selected wavelength spanning the range of the visible spectrum of light.

Wavelength λ	Color Absorbed	Color Observed
380 - 430 nm	Blue-Violet	Yellow
430 - 500 nm	Blue	Orange
500 - 520 nm	Blue-Green	Red
520 - 565 nm	Green	Purple
565 - 590 nm	Yellow	Blue-Violet
590 - 625 nm	Orange	Blue
625 - 740 nm	Red	Blue-Green

The axes in the plot in Figure 1-1 are labeled absorption A and wavelength λ. The wavelength of light provides a measure of its frequency ν, since the product of wavelength and frequency result in the speed of light c. The speed of light is an important physical constant, and the speed of all electromagnetic radiation, including visible light, in a vacuum is 3.00×10^8 m/s. Therefore, the frequency of light can be calculated as $\nu = c/\lambda$, and using the relationship $\Delta E = h\nu$, we get $\Delta E = (h \times c)/\lambda$ for the energy of electromagnetic radiation.

The absorbance A is a measure of a loss in intensity when light travels through a certain medium.

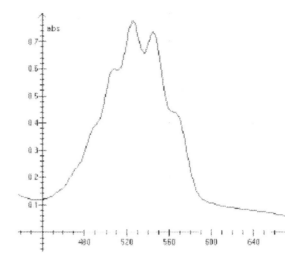

Figure 10-1: Visible Absorption Spectrum of Permanganate Ion.

The process of absorption can be understood in the following way. A beam of light consists of a stream of photons. When a beam of light travels through a solution of a given substance, a photon might encounter a certain molecule in solution, and there is a chance the molecule will absorb the photon. This absorption reduces the number of photons in the beam of light, thereby reducing the intensity of the light beam. *The solution absorbs light* is the terminology used to describe this process, which is schematically illustrated in Figure 10-2.

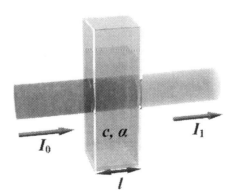

Figure 10-2: Absorption and intensity loss of a light beam

If we designate the intensity of the incident light as I_0, and the intensity of the transmitted light as $I1$ the ratio I_1/I_0 is called **transmittance** T. The transmittance of a solution is the fraction of the original light that passes through the sample. Many spectrophotometric devices also measure the more conveniently-used property **absorbance** A, which is directly related to transmittance, equation 10.1:

$$A = -\log T \qquad \text{(10.1)}$$

The absorbance A of a sample depends on the concentration c of the solution, on the length l of the path the light beam travels through the solution, and on substance-specific constant, the *molar absorptivity* coefficient ε, equation 10.2.

$$A = \varepsilon \cdot l \cdot c \qquad \text{(10.2)}$$

In the older literature, ε was known as the extinction coefficient. The resulting equation 10.2 is commonly known as **Lambert Beer Law**.

The molar absorptivity coefficient depends not only the natur of the absorbing molecule, but also on the wavelength of the light whose absorption is measured; its units are $M^{-1} \cdot cm^{-1}$.

Lambert Beer Law establishes a straight-line relationship between the absorbance of a solution A and its concentration c. In its common formulation, equation 10.2, the absorbance is expressed as a function of concentration, $A = f(c)$. This form is used when the emphasis of a series of absorption measurements is the evaluation of the *molar absorptivity* coefficient ε. If on the other hand absorption measurements are employed to determine concentrations of solutions, an inverted form of The Lambert Beer Law, in which concentration is expressed as a function of absorbance, $c = f(A)$, provides a more convenient alternative.

The absorption of electromagnetic radiation is measured with a device called **spectrophotometer**. Spectrophotometers that measure the absorption of radiation in the infrared, ultraviolet, and visible regions all are available. A schematic showing the basic components of a spectrophotometer is displayed in Figure 10-3.

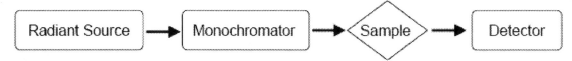

Figure 10-3: Spectrophotometer Schematic

Continuous radiation from a suitable *radiant source* is first separated into its component wavelengths with a *monochromator*. A beam of radiation of selected wavelength is then passed through a *sample* contained in a sample cell or cuvette. A *detector* on the other side of the sample cell converts the unabsorbed radiant energy to an electrical signal, which is processed and displayed. The absorption spectrum shown in Figure 10-1 was taken with an instrument capable of scanning over a range of wavelengths while continuously monitoring absorption. In applications dealing with concentration determination from absorption measurements, spectrophotometric devices that operate at a number of selected wavelengths only, are sometimes used.

Beer's law, equation 10.2, can be used in its inverted form to determine the concentration of an *analyte*, which is the substance in an analysis that is being identified or determined. Beer's law, which describes absorption as a function of concentration, is rearranged, and concentration is expressed as a function of absorbance, equation 10.3.

$$c = A/(\varepsilon \cdot l) \tag{10.3}$$

A series of standard solutions, e.g. solutions with accurately known analyte concentration, is prepared. The absorbance of each solution is measured, and a working curve is constructed from a plot of absorbance versus concentration. A trendline is fitted to the data points. Ideally, the trendline will run through the origin of the coordinate system; a solution where the concentration of analyte is zero cannot absorb light at a wavelength characteristic for the analyte. An unknown concentration of a solution can then be calculated from its measured absorbance and the equation of the trendline. Examples of a calibration curve and an absorbance-concentration plot are shown in Figure 10-4.

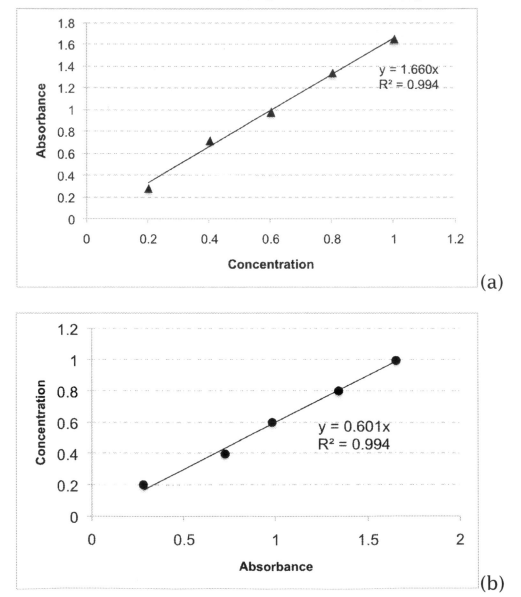

(a)

(b)

Figure 10-4: Examples of (a) a calibration curve and (b) an absorbance-concentration plot.

Permanganate is a suitable species for absorption spectrophotometry due to its intense color and high absorbtivity. Permanganate is also a strong oxidiant, and measuring the concentration change of permanganate allows us in turn to determine the concentration of a reductant.

In this experiment, we will determine the concentration of an oxalic acid solution. Oxalic acid is a chemical compound with formula $C_2H_2O_4$. It is a dicarboxylic acid that is better described with the condensed structural formula HOOC-COOH, which indicates the presence of two carboxyl groups (-COOH). Oxalic acid is a relatively strong organic acid, being about 10,000 times stronger than acetic acid. Furthermore, oxalic acid is a *reducing agent*. Among the many uses of oxalic acid are household chemical products such as Bar Keeper's Friend (a powdered household cleaner sold for use particularly on metals), wood restorers, and additives to automotive wheel cleaners.

In acidic solution, the reducing agent oxalic acid reacts with the oxidizing agent permanganate ion. Oxalic acid is oxidized to carbon dioxide, whereas the purple permanganate ion MnO_4^- is reduced to the (almost) colorless Mn^{2+} cation. The stoichiometry of this redox reaction is given in equation 10.4:

$$2\ MnO_4^- + 5\ C_2H_2O_4 + 6\ H^+ \rightarrow 2\ Mn^{2+} + 10\ CO_2 + 8\ H_2O \tag{10.4}$$

From equation 10.4 we infer that 5 moles of oxalic acid are oxidized by 2 moles of permanganate, yielding the following relationship:

$$\frac{n_{C_2H_2O_4}}{n_{MnO_4^-}} = \frac{5}{2} \tag{10.5}$$

A well defined amount of a permanganate solution with a known concentration is added to a well defined amount of oxalic acid solution of unknown concentration. Further, a well defined amount of sulfuric acid, $V_{H_2SO_4}^{add}$, is added to the reaction mixture. On occasion, the oxalic acid solution in aqueous solution is initially transformed into an oxalic acid solution in acidic solution, and it is not necessary to further add sulfuric acid, $V_{H_2SO_4}^{add}=0$. Although the concentration of the permanganate solution will change due to dilution, the number of moles remains the same. The number of moles of permanganate present at the beginning of the redox reaction is obtained as

$$n_{MnO_4^-}^{initial} = c_{MnO_4^-}^{initial} \times V_{MnO_4^-}^{initial} \tag{10.6}$$

MnO_4^- is added in excess, so that not the entire amount of permanganate ion will be consumed in the redox reaction. The final concentration of permanganate at the end of the redox reaction is determined from its absorption, and from the final concentration, one can calculate the remaining number of moles of permanganate:

$$n_{MnO_4^-}^{final} = c_{MnO_4^-}^{final} \times (V_{MnO_4^-}^{initial} + V_{C_2H_2O_4}^{initial} + V_{H_2SO_4}^{add}) \tag{10.7}$$

The amount of oxalic acid that reacted with permanganate is calculated from the difference in the number of moles of permanganate, and from the stoichiometric relationship given in equation 10.5:

$$n_{C_2H_2O_4} = \frac{5}{2}(n_{MnO_4^-}^{initial} - n_{MnO_4^-}^{final}) \tag{10.8}$$

The number of moles of oxalic acid together with the volume of oxalic acid solution that was added to the reaction mixture allows one to calculate the unknown concentration of the oxalic acid solution:

$$c_{C_2H_2O_4} = \frac{n_{C_2H_2O_4}}{V^{initial}_{C_2H_2O_4}}$$

(10.9)

The reduction of permanganate by oxalic acid is an example of **catalysis**, and more specifically, of **autocatalysis.** *Catalysis* itself is the acceleration or increase in rate of a chemical reaction by means of a substance called a **catalyst**, which is itself not consumed by the overall reaction. A single chemical reaction is said to have undergone *autocatalysis*, or be *autocatalytic*, if the reaction product itself is the catalyst for that reaction. The reduction of permanganate by oxalic acid initially proceeds slowly, but the rate gradually increases because the product Mn^{2+} is an effective catalyst for this reaction. One can make use of this effect, and enhance the reaction rate by adding a small catalytic amount of manganese(II) ion to the reaction mixture.

10.3 Procedure

Absorptions are measured with a single-beam spectrophotometer, and the following instructions refer to the S42669PKND Fisher Educational Spectrophotometer. The general principles outlined apply to other spectrophotometers, such as the SPEC20, as well.

10.3.1 Calibration of the instrument

The instrument needs to be calibrated for measurements at a wavelength of 525 nm, which corresponds to the maximum absorption wavelength of permanganate ion. The procedure described below is called *blanking.* Blanking must be done each time a new wavelength is selected. The step-by-step procedure for setting up the spectrophotometer is as follows:

1. Turn on the spectrophotometer. Allow the instrument to warm up for at least 15 minutes in order to stabilize the lamp and detector

2. Push the %T/A selector to choose the A (Absorbance) operating mode.

3. Turn the wavelength control knob to 525nm.

4. Move the second order filter lever position to the appropriate filter setting. For measurements at 525nm, pull out the second order filter lever until the green dot is showing.

5. Fill a cuvette with blanking solution. Here, we use de-ionized water as blanking solution. If you use a 1 cm square cuvette, fill the cuvette almost completely, and insert the cuvette into the cuvette holder. Make sure that you position the cuvette correctly in the cuvette holder, so that the light beam enters and leaves the cuvette through its clear and plain faces. Place the cuvette holder into the sample compartment. Be sure that the cuvette holder has been firmly pressed into the sample compartment and the lid of the sample compartment has been closed. If you use a tubular test tube cuvette, fill the cuvette 2/3 full with blanking solution. Place the test tube cuvette into the sample compartment. Be sure the test tube cuvette has been firmly pressed into the sample compartment and the lid of the sample compartment has been closed.

6. Adjust the display to 0.00A by turning the 100%T/A control.

7. Remove the cuvette from the sample compartment.

10.3.2 Calibration curve for permanganate

Place five dry and clean 18×150mm test tubes into a test tube rack; label the test tubes 1, 2, 3, 4, and 5.

Add 5.0 mL of 3.0 mM potassium permanganate solution and 15 mL of de-ionized water to test tube #1.

Add 4.0 mL of 3.0 mM potassium permanganate solution and 16 mL of de-ionized water to test tube #2.

Add 3.0 mL of 3.0 mM potassium permanganate solution and 17 mL of de-ionized water to test tube #3.

Add 2.0 mL of 3.0 mM potassium permanganate solution and 18 mL of de-ionized water to test tube #4.

Add 1.0 mL of 3.0 mM potassium permanganate solution and 19 mL of de-ionized water to test tube #5.

Make sure that you gently swirl test tubes 1-5 in order to mix their contents and to produce a homogeneous solution.

Measure the absorbance A at 525 nm for each of the five solutions. First, rinse a cuvette with a small amount (0.5 to 1.0 mL) of the permanganate solution. Then, if you use a 1 cm square cuvette, fill the cuvette almost completely with permanganate solution, and insert the cuvette into the cuvette holder. Make sure that you position the cuvette correctly in the cuvette holder, so that the light beam enters and leaves the cuvette through its clear and plain faces. Place the cuvette holder into the sample compartment. Be sure that the cuvette holder has been firmly pressed into the sample compartment and the lid of the sample compartment has been closed. If you use a tubular test tube cuvette, fill the cuvette 2/3 full with permanganate solution. Place the test tube cuvette into the sample compartment. Be sure the test tube cuvette has been firmly pressed into the sample compartment and the lid of the sample compartment has been closed. In your notebook, record the absorbance reading for each of the five solutions. You might want to use a table to record your results:

#	3.0 mM MnO_4^-	H_2O	Absorbance A
1	5.0 mL	15.0 mL	
2	4.0 mL	16.0 mL	

All extra solution and chemical waste is to be properly disposed of in the appropriate waste containers placed in the fume hood.

10.3.3 Concentration of an Oxalic acid solution

Obtain three dry and clean 125 mL Erlenenmeyer flasks; label the flasks 1, 2, and 3.

To flask #1, add 2 mL of potassium permanganate solution, 19.5 mL of de-ionized water, 4 mL of unknown oxalic acid solution, and 2 mL of 1M H_2SO_4.

To flask #2, add 2 mL of potassium permanganate solution, 19.5 mL of de-ionized water, 4 mL of unknown oxalic acid solution, 2 mL of 1M H_2SO_4 and a very small scoop of manganese(II) sulfate powder.

To flask #3, add 2 mL of potassium permanganate solution, 21.5 mL of deionized water, 2 mL of unknown oxalic acid solution, 2 mL of 1M H_2SO_4 and a very small scoop of manganese(II) sulfate powder.

Swirl the contents of the flasks, and let the redox reaction proceed for at least 7 minutes. Monitor the changes in color. Record your observations in your lab notebook.

Use a Pasteur pipette, and fill a cuvette with the reaction mixture of flask 3. Measure the absorption at 525nm of the solution of flask 3. Record the absorption in your lab notebook.

Repeat this procedure for the solutions of flasks 2 and 1, and record their absorption values in your lab notebook.

10.4 Calculations

10.4.1 Calibration Curve

For the calibration curve, calculate the concentrations of the $KMnO_4$ solutions of test tubes 1 to 5. Set up a concentration-absorbance table:

Test Tube #	Concentration	Absorbance
1		
2		
3		
4		
5		

Use a spreadsheet program such as Excel to construct an absorbance-concentration plot (see Figure 10-4). Fit a trendline to your set of data, and set the intercept to be zero. Record the equation of the trendline. Add a print-out of your plot as part of your lab-report.

From the slope of your trendline, obtain values for $1/(\varepsilon \cdot l)$ and for the molar absorptivity coefficient ε. Assume a length of 1cm for the cuvette you have used. Report the values of $1/(\varepsilon \cdot l)$ and ε with the *correct units*.

10.4.2 Concentration of the oxalic acid solution

For each of the three redox reactions carried out in Erlenmeyer flasks 1 to 3, calculate the permanganate concentration at the end of the redox reaction according to equation 10.3, using absorbance values and the value of $1/(\varepsilon \cdot l)$ obtained in section 10.4.1.

Calculate the number of moles of oxalic acid consumed during the redox reaction from the concentration at the end of the reaction, and from the initial concentration.

For each of the three reactions, calculate the unknown concentration of the oxalic acid solution.

Use equations 10.6 to 10.9 to calculate moles of permanganate, moles of oxalic acid, and concentration of oxalic acid. Collect your results in a proper table:

Trial #	A	$c_{MnO_4^-}^{final}$	$n_{MnO_4^-}^{final}$	$n_{MnO_4^-}^{initial}$	$n_{C_2H_2O_4}$	$c_{C_2H_2O_4}$
1						
2						
3						

10.5 Discussion

The discussion should address among others the following points:

i) Do the observations support an autocatalytic process?

ii) Do the observations support the fact that Mn^{2+} acts as catalyst for the redox reaction?

iii) Are your the results reproducible, that is are the three concentration values obtained close to each other within reasonable range?

EXPERIMENT 11: Paper Chromatography — Separation of Plant Pigments

11.1 Purpose

In experiment 11, plant pigments dissolved in an organic solvent extract will be separated by using chromatographic techniques.

11.2 Background

In 1906 the Russian botanist Mikhail Semyonovich Tsvet extracted the plant pigments that produce the fall colors in leaves by grinding them up in a solvent (coincidentally, *tsvet* is Russian for both *color* as well as *flowering*). When he poured the solvent extract containing the mixture of dissolved pigments through a tube full of powdered chalk, that is $CaCO^3$ or calcium carbonate, the various pigments separated into colored bands as the extract flowed down through the powdered chalk by gravity flow. He carefully removed the column of chalk from the tube and separated the colored bands. The different colored bands were subjected to extraction with additional solvent. Solutions of the separated pigments were obtained in this way. Tsvett termed this new technique **chromatography**, which literally means "color writing". Since its discovery chromatography has become a vital tool for separating organic and inorganic compounds, and is used as analytical method as well as on a preparative scale.

In all forms of *chromatography* there is a **mobile phase** and a **stationary phase**, and *chromatography* is based on the partition equilibrium for a given solute between the two phases. The *mobile phase* moves through the stationary phase from one end to the other, carrying the substance of interest with it. A solute — a compound that is dissolved in a solvent — with a greater affinity for the mobile phase will spend more time in this phase than a solute that prefers the stationary phase. Thus, different solutes that move through the stationary phase separate from one-another.

The stationary phase for most chromatographic separations is usually a solid, and this method is referred to as *adsorption* chromatography. The mobile phase can either be a liquid or a gas, and the corresponding chromatographic techniques are termed *liquid chromatography* and *gas chromatography*, respectively. A technique, in which a liquid serves both as stationary phase and as mobile phase is referred to as *liquid-liquid partition* chromatography.

In this experiment, a form of adsorption chromatography known as **paper chromatography** will be used to extract colored components from a plant extract. Paper chromatography is a useful technique for separating and identifying pigments and other molecules from cell extracts that contain a complex mixture of molecules. The stationary phase in paper chromatography is a strip of paper, which then is placed in a solvent. Only one end of the paper strip is in contact with the solvent reservoir. The solvent moves up the paper by capillary action, which occurs as a result of the attraction of solvent molecules to the paper and the attraction of the solvent molecules to one another. As the solvent moves up the paper, it carries along any substances dissolved in it.

The solutes are carried along at different rates for two main reasons: i) different substances are not equally soluble in the solvent that comprises the mobile phase, and ii) different substances are attracted to different degrees to the fibers of the paper through intermolecular forces. The intermolecular forces that are possibly of importance are hydrogen bonding, dipole-dipole interactions, or dispersion forces. If we can identify the intermolecular forces present between the solutes and the different chromatographic phases, such as the stationary phase and the mobile phase, one can then rationalize the order in which substances will travel through a given stationary phase.

Paper is composed of intertwined fibers of *cellulose*. The cellulose molecule is a *polymer*, meaning that the molecule as a whole is made up of many repeating units linked together. A portion of a cellulose molecule is shown in Figure 11-1:

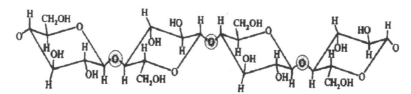

Figure 11-1: Schematic representation of a portion of a cellulose polymer unit.

While the structure of cellulose is quite complex, we will only concentrate on the hydroxyl (-OH) groups that are part of the molecule. Since hydrogen is bonded to a highly electronegative element, the O-H bond is polarized, and the opportunity for dipole-dipole interactions and more specifically for hydrogen bonding interactions exists with other polar molecules which may venture into the vicinity of a cellulose molecule.

While a large number of pigments exist in plants, four pigments that can be extracted from green leaves are of particular interest, namely *chlorophyll* a, *chlorophyll* b, *β-carotene*, and *xanthophyll*. Molecular formulas of these compounds are displayed in Figure 11-2.

The compounds introduced above are of special interest for this experiment since i) they are present in relatively large amounts in green leaves, ii) they have characteristic colors and can be detected visually, and iii) they have distinct structural features that allow us to predict and rationalize their migration order in a paper chromatography experiment. The characteristic colors are bright-green/blue-green for chlorophyll *a*, olive-green for chlorophyll *b*, yellow-orange for β-carotene, and yellow for xanthophyll.

When we scrutinize the structures of the pigments as shown in Figure 11-2, we notice that both chlorophyll *a* and chlorophyll *b* posses several carbonyl groups (-C=O), in which a terminal oxygen atom is bonded to a central carbon atom. Since the C=O double bond is a polar bond due to the electronegativity difference between the two elements, the chlorophyll molecule as a whole can be expected to be polar. Further, we notice that the two forms of chlorophyll are identical except for the presence of an additional carbonyl group in chlorophyll *b* (compare the boxed structural element in Figure 11-2). Thus, we can expect chlorophyll *b* to be slightly more polar than chlorophyll *a*. When inspecting the structure of β-carotene, we find that this molecule only has a hydrocarbon skeleton, and is therefore essentially non-polar. The structure of xanthophyll is very similar to that of β-carotene, the difference being the presence of two polar hydroxyl (-OH) groups (compare the boxed structural

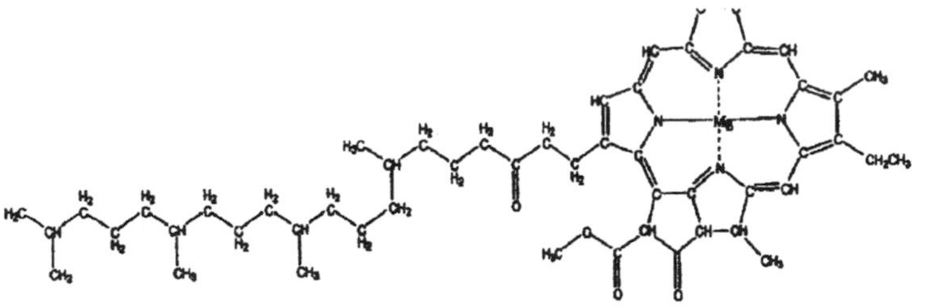

chlorophyll *a*

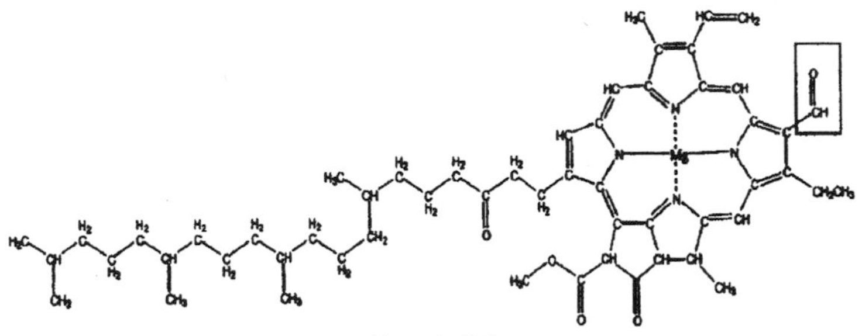

chlorophyll *b*

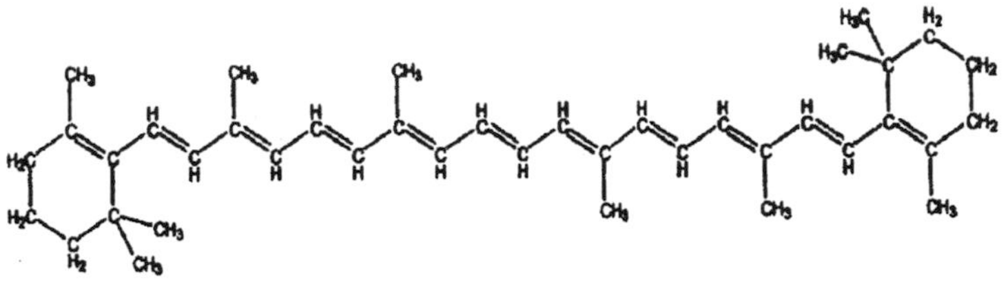

β-carotene

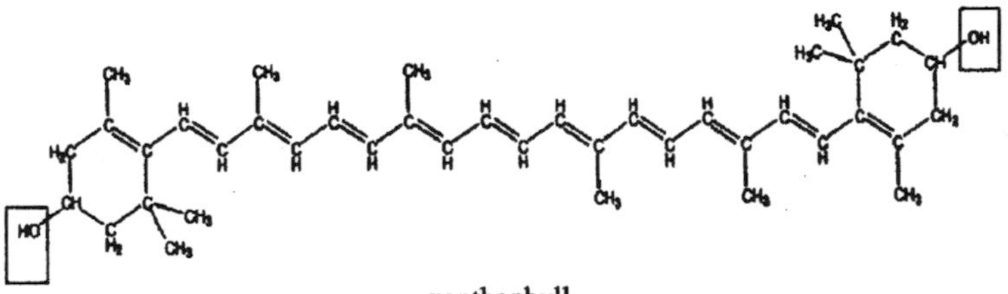

xanthophyll

Figure 11-2: Molecular formulas of four representative plant pigments.

elements in Figure 11-2). We therefore expect xanthophyll to be more polar than β-carotene.

When a mixture of the pigments dissolved in an organic solvent is applied to a piece of paper, all pigments will have some attraction or affinity for the cellulose, be it from dipole-dipole interactions or dispersion interactions. The pigments which have some degree of polarity will be attracted to the paper more strongly than the non-polar pigments, since dipole-dipole interactions and hydrogen bonding interactions exist between a pigment molecule and the cellulose. The mobile phase is either non-polar or polar to certain degree. Conveniently, a mixture of a polar solvent and a non-polar solvent is employed as mobile phase. By varying the composition of the mobile phase its polar character can be accordingly adjusted. In this experiment, heptane (C_7H_{13}) constitutes a non-polar component, and acetone ($CH_3C(O)CH_3$) constitutes a polar component of the mobile phase.

heptane   acetone

As the chromatogram *develops*, we notice that the solvent is slowly working its way through the paper, and that several bands of different color and separated from one-another begin to appear. Depending on the polarity of the solvent that is used, each band of color may either i) not move at all from the *starting point*, ii) completely keep up with the migrating *solvent front* or iii) move at a rate somewhat slower than the solvent front. The **retention factor R_f** is a quantitative indication of how far a particular compound travels in a particular solvent. The retention factor R_f is defined as ratio of the distance D_s the solute moves and distance Dsf traveled by the solvent front, equation 11.1.

$$R_f = D_S/D_{sf}$$

(11.1)

A schematic representation of a chromatogram is shown in Figure 11-3.

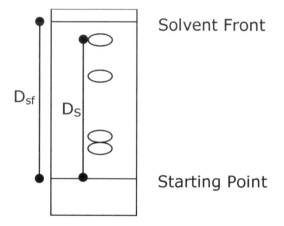

Figure 11-3: Schematic representation of a developed chromatogram indicating relevant traveled distances.

For any given chromatographic system, the R_f value is a characteristic property of a molecule. It can be used as an indicator of whether an unknown compound and a known compound are similar, if not identical. As can be seen from the definition given in equation 1.1, the retention factor takes on values of between zero and one: $0 \leq R_f \leq 1$.

Arguments based on intermolecular forces are helpful in illustrating the importance of the retention factor. As mentioned above, the partition equilibrium of a solute between the mobile phase and the stationary phase is one of the important characteristics of any chromatography experiment, since solute molecules can only migrate when in the mobile phase. Thus, we can expect that pigments which have a higher affinity for the mobile phase than for the stationary phase will move faster through the paper. The affinity for a particular phase is determined by the presence of intermolecular forces. Intermolecular forces that are generally present but that are weak are dispersion forces and dipole-induced-dipole forces. In addition, if polar groups are present in the molecule and either one of the chromatographic phases, there exist dipole-dipole interactions and possibly hydrogen bonding interactions, both of which are considerably stronger than dispersion and dipole-induced forces. Affinity differences for either the stationary phase or the mobile phase can be argued by considering the different polar character of these phases. When separating molecules with different polarities, it is to be expected that the more polar molecules will be more strongly attracted to the more polar phase. All of the effects discussed above lead to the common statement that "like dissolves like"; that is, polar solvents will dissolve polar solutes and non-polar solvents will dissolve non-polar solutes. We can expect that, when working with a polar stationary phase and a polar mobile phase, polar molecules will have an R_f value of closer to one, while when working with a polar stationary phase and a non-polar mobile phase, polar molecules will have an R_f value of closer to zero. The opposite conclusions are reached when considering non-polar molecules that travel through a polar stationary phase under the influence of either a polar or non-polar mobile phase.

11.3 Procedure

Before you begin your experiment, predict the order in which the plant pigments *chlorophyll* a, *chlorophyll* b, *β-carotene*, and *xanthophylls* will migrate through the paper for each of the pure solvents heptane and acetone. Report your hypothesis in your lab notebook.

11.3.1 Preparing reaction chambers: Set out two 150 ml beakers on your desktop, transfer 3 ml of heptane into the first beaker and 3 ml of acetone into the second, and gently swirl the contents to get solvent on the sides of the beaker too. Then cover each beaker with a watchglass. This will allow the chamber to fill with evaporated solvent over time, which will help facilitate the smooth movement of the mobile phase. It further prevents the liquid from *stalling* by slowing down the rate at which it evaporates off the paper, a process detrimental to any chromatography experiment. This is also the reason why it is important to keep the opening of the beaker covered as much of the time as possible. Place the chromatography chambers under the fume cabinet for later use.

11.3.2 Preparation of the pigment extract: Rip a green leaf into small pieces. Leaves of any deciduous trees or vegetable leafes like spinach leaves all are suitable. Grind the leaf for about 5 to 10 minutes with a mortar and pestle in 5 ml of ethyl acetate until the solution is a dark green color. Since the extraction solvent will partly evaporate, it might be necessary to add a small amount of ethyl acetate from time to time. Decant the solution into a 50 ml beaker, being careful to separate the leaves from the solution.

11.3.3 Making a glass micro-capillary: In this experiment it is essential to make the initial solute spots as concentrated and small as possible. While capillary tube openings themselves are in fact very small, for the purpose this experiment even they may be too large to make good spots on the chromatographic paper. Set up a Bunsen burner, make sure there is nothing flammable near the Bunsen burner set up, and place all items needed for preparation of micro-capillaries away from your current work area. Follow the four steps outlined below, and draw a micro-capillary:

a) Adjust the flame of the Bunsen burner so that an inner blue cone is present. Lightly hold a capillary tube by each end, but *only by the ends!*

b) While slowly rolling the tube back and forth between thumb and forefinger, gently lower the capillary tube into the flame such that the center of the tube touches the inner blue cone.

c) Continue to roll the tube and also slowly pull the ends of the tube outward. At first there will be very little movement, but then the glass will quickly come apart. Let the glass cool for a moment.

d) *Carefully*, with the tip of your spatula, break off the tip of each *needle-like* end. Dispose of excess glass properly. This procedure yields two micro-capillaries. The holes of the micro capillaries are extremely small, so be sure not to poke a hole into the chromatographic paper when transferring the concentration pigment solution.

The four steps in making a micro-capillary tube described above are illustrated in Figure 11-4.

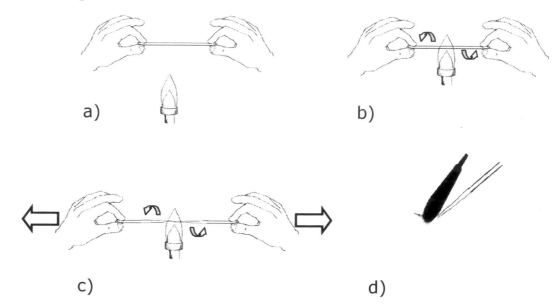

a)   b)

c)   d)

Figure 11-4: Steps in making a micro-capillary tube.

11.3.4 Set-up of the chromatographic paper: Obtain two 10 cm long strips of chromatography paper and a micro-capillary. With a **pencil,** draw *starting lines* on the chromatography papers about 1cm from one end and use the glass micro-capillary to transfer a small amount of the leaf extract onto the line. Lightly tap the surface of the paper to prevent tearing. It will be necessary to transfer solution several times in order to produce a spot which is easily visible on the paper. Since the spot should be as small as possible, let the solvent evaporate between transfers.

11.3.5 Chromatographic separation: For each of the prepared chromatography strips make a fold about 1 cm from the end of the chromatography paper opposite to the starting line. Remove the watchglass from a beaker, place the paper with its fold over the rim of the beaker, and secure it with watchglass. Make sure that the paper is in contact with the solvent contained in the beaker, and that the solvent level is below the starting pencil mark. The set-up of the chromatography chamber is illustrated in Figure 11-5.

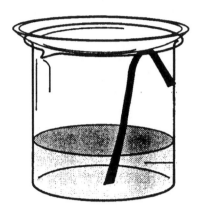

Figure 11-5: Set-up of a chromatography chamber.

The solvent should start moving through the paper by capillary action, and you should allow the chromatogram to develop until the solvent front is about 1 cm from the watchglass. Then quickly remove the paper from the beaker and draw a line on the paper indicating the point where the solvent front has reached. Allow the paper to dry and draw circles around any colored spots seen on the chromatography paper. Measure Dsf and Ds values; the Ds values are to be measured from the center of the colored spot. Record these values in your laboratory notebook. Identify each spot by color, report the colors and note the migration characteristics as well as migration order for each chromatogram in your laboratory notebook. It is important that this step is completed before the colors fade away. Draw pictures of the chromatograms into your lab notebook for future reference.

11.3.6 Chromatography with solvents of different polarity: Repeat the step described in sections 11.3.1, 11.3.4 and 11.3.5 with mobile phases that are 20 vol% acetone and 80 vol% heptane, as well as 60 vol% acetone and 40 vol% heptane. The mobile phase solutions are prepared by combining 1ml acetone and 4ml heptane, and 3ml acetone and 2ml heptane using a 10 ml graduated cylinder, respectively. Based on these chromatograms, propose a ratio for the mobile phase mixture of heptane and acetone that might yield a better separation. Prepare about 5 mL of this new mobile phase mixture, perform the chromatography experiment, and test whether your proposal is verified. The procedure in section 11.3.3 only needs to be repeated if additional micro-capillaries are required.

11.4 Calculations

Calculate the retention factor R_f for each solute in each of the solvents used as mobile phase.

11.5 Discussion

The discussion should address among others the following points:

i) State and explain your original hypothesis regarding the migration order and whether or not your results support this hypothesis.

ii) If the original prediction is not supported by your data, modify your hypothesis to account for the experimental results.

iii) Comment on a correlation between Rf and the polarity of organic molecules. Explain why with solvents of different polarity a better separation of the different pigments is achieved.

iv) Identify the solvent system that is most suitable for separating the different pigments, explain why, and suggest possible improvements for the separation of color pigments extracted from green leaves.

v) Discuss the drawbacks of the other solvent systems used.

EXPERIMENT 12: Colligative Properties — Freezing Point Depression

12.1 Purpose

In experiment 12, the freezing point depression constant for water will be evaluated and used to determine the molecular weight of a given substance.

12.2 Background

The freezing point and the boiling point of a solvent are affected by the addition of a solute. The amount by which the freezing point is depressed or the boiling point is elevated depends on the nature of the solvent, the amount of solvent, and the number of particles of solute, but it does not depend on the nature of the solute. Since the magnitude of the boiling point elevation and freezing point depression is the same regardless of the identity of the solute, boiling point elevation and freezing point depression are called **colligative properties**.

Suppose that the freezing point of a pure substance is some temperature T_{FP}. At the freezing point, an *equilibrium* exists between the solid state and the liquid state. Thus, the overall rate at which liquid freezes must equal the rate at which solid melts. If one rate were faster than the other then one of two things would happen: i) the solid would melt as more molecules went into the liquid, shifting the equilibrium irreversibly to the liquid state, or ii) the liquid would freeze as more molecules aggregate to the surface of the solid, shifting the equilibrium irreversibly to the solid state.

This equilibrium is illustrated in Figure 12-1. At any given time, a certain number of molecules $N_{S \to L}$ will break away from the solid compound and migrate into the surrounding liquid phase. At the same time, a certain number of molecules $N_{L \to S}$ that are part of the liquid collective surrounding the solid, and that are in close vicinity to the solid compound, will aggregate with the solid. At temperature T_{FP}, the numbers $N_{S \to L}$ and $N_{L \to S}$ are equal. The processes described here represent what is commonly understood as *melting* and *freezing*, respectively.

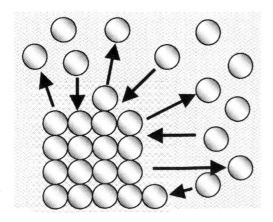

Figure 12-1: Melting/Freezing Equilibrium at T_{FP}

Figure 12-2 shows a typical **cooling curve** of a liquid. In a cooling curve, the change in temperature of the system is monitored over time. Initially, the temperature of the liquid constantly decreases. The horizontal line indicates the measured freezing point of the liquid. At this point, solid and liquid coexist. As one continues to remove heat from the system, more and more liquid freezes. Once all liquid has frozen, the temperature of the solid begins to drop.

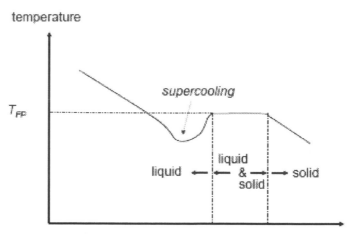

Figure 12-2: Cooling curve of a pure liquid

Also shown in Figure 12-2 is the effect of **supercooling**, which is the process of chilling a liquid below its freezing point. The temperature of the liquid falls below the actual freezing point, before crystals begin to form. Once the liquid begins to crystallize, the temperature rises abruptly due to the energy released during crystallization. To prevent supercooling, a seed crystal or nucleus around which a crystal structure can form is added to a liquid. Many liquids show supercooling when they are undergoing crystallization.

We will now consider a situation in which a solute is added to the liquid phase of a solid/liquid system at T_{FP}. This situation is schematically illustrated in Figure 12-3. Solute molecules are replacing solvent molecules in the liquid collective surrounding the solid. The rate with which molecules leave the solid compound is not affected by the addition of solute to the liquid phase. However, the rate at which molecules are added back to the surface is lower because there are now fewer solvent molecules surrounding the solid due to the presence of the solute molecules. The solid/liquid equilibrium at T_{FP} is disturbed, and will eventually and invariable shift to the liquid phase – the presence of the solute causes the solid phase to melt completely.

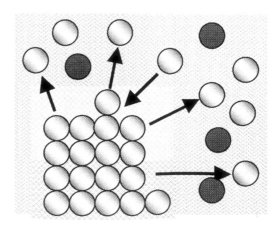

Figure 12-3: The presence of a solute disturbs the Melting/Freezing Equilibrium at T_{FP}.

To compensate for the presence of the solute, the rates, and especially the rate at which the solid melts, need to be lowered. The rates for the melting and freezing processes are temperature dependent, since they depend on the molecular motion and the average molecular kinetic energy. Since the average molecular energy is proportional to the Kelvin temperature, the rate will decrease when the temperature is lowered. Thus, in the presence of a solvent the melting/freezing equilibrium is re-established at a temperature lower than the normal freezing point T_{FP}. In other words, the freezing point of the solution is depressed due to the addition of solute, because the presence of the solute interferes with the rate at which the liquid freezes. The depressed freezing point temperature is referred to as T_{FP}^{depr}. The **freezing point depression** ΔT_f is then defined as the difference between the depressed freezing point of the solution and the freezing point of the pure solvent (equation 12.1).

$$\Delta T_F = T_{FP}^{depr} - T_{FP} \qquad\qquad\qquad (12.1)$$

A number of complications exist when measuring freezing point depressions ΔT_f. One complication is that the solute concentration increases as the solution freezes. Since the solution becomes more concentrated as the solvent freezes, the freezing point of the solution continues to drop. Therefore, when measuring freezing point depressions, the initial freezing temperature — that is the temperature describing the onset of the freezing process — is taken as the characteristic temperature. After the solvent starts to freeze we no longer know the precise concentration of the solution.

The cooling curve of a solution has a different appearance than the cooling curve of the pure solvent. An exemplarily cooling curve is shown in Figure 12-4. The curve does not become horizontal at the freezing point. Rather, a "kink" or discontinuity occurs at the freezing point. This discontinuity may be obscured by supercooling. If so, the characteristic temperature can be determined by extrapolation. This situation is illustrated in Figure 12-4. If no supercooling occurs, the characteristic temperature is the temperature at the onset of crystallization.

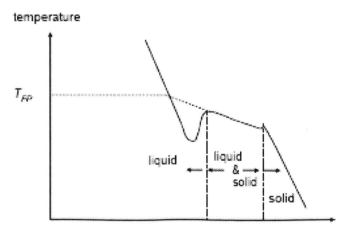

Figure 12-4: Cooling curve of a solution with supercooling.

The reason that the cooling curve is not horizontal at the freezing point is that as the solution freezes, the composition of the liquid changes. The solid phase, which forms at the freezing point, is pure solvent. Consequently, as freezing occurs, the concentration of the solution increases, and the freezing point decreases.

The second complication is that measuring the concentration of a solution by using *molarity* does not provide a convenient unit of measurement when discussing colligative properties. A more appropriate concentration unit for freezing point depression is **molality**. *Molality* M_m is defined as the *number of moles* of solute, *n*, per mass dissolved in one kilogram of solvent, equation 12.2:

$$M_m = \frac{n_{solute}}{m_{solvent}} \tag{12.2}$$

Molalities are usually referenced to 1kg of solvent. If, for example, 4 mol of solute are dissolved in 1kg of solvent, the concentration or *molality* of the resulting solution is referred to as being "4 molal".

There are two important differences between molality and molarity: i) The definition of *molality* is based on the *mass* of solvent, whereas the definition of *molarity* is based on the *volume* of solution. ii) Mass does not change with temperature, whereas volume of a solution will change slightly with temperature. Thus, the molality of a solution remains the same when the temperature is changed, but the same cannot be said of the molarity of a solution.

As stated above, freezing point depression ΔT_f depends only on the nature of the solvent, the amount of solvent, and the number of particles of solute. This statement is formulated in equation 12.3:

$$\Delta T_f = -K_f \cdot M_m \tag{12.3}$$

The amount of solvent and the number of particles of solute define the molality M_m, whereas the *freezing point depression constant* K_f is a characteristic constant of the solvent, and depends on the nature of the solvent.

Equation 12.3 is based on the assumption that for every mole of solute that dissolves, one mole of particles goes into solution. There exist, however, many substances for which this assumption does not hold true. Ionic substances like NaCl or Na_2SO_4, or molecular substances that ionize in water like HCl or CH_3COOH, result in more than one mole of particles for each mole of substance dissolved. This deviation from the behavior of non-ionizing solutes, like glucose $C_6H_{12}O_6$ or acetone $CH_3C(O)CH_3$, is accounted for by determining the number of particles a substance forms as it dissolves. The corresponding correction factor is called the *van't Hoff number i*. A corrected expression for freezing point depression is given in equation 12.4:

$$\Delta T_f = -i \cdot K_f \cdot M_m \tag{12.4}$$

In equations 12.5 to 12.7, representative chemical equations with their corresponding van't Hoff numbers are given:

$$C_6H_{12}O_6(s) \xrightarrow{H_2O} C_6H_{12}O_6(aq) \qquad i = 1 \tag{12.5}$$

$$HCl(g) \xrightarrow{H_2O} H^+(aq) + Cl^-(aq) \quad i = 2 \tag{12.6}$$

$$Na_2SO_4(s) \xrightarrow{H_2O} 2Na^+ + SO_4^{2-}(aq) \quad i = 3 \tag{12.7}$$

The van't Hoff number *i* is the number of moles of solute actually in solution per mole of solid solute added. For non-ionizing molecules like glucose $C_6H_{12}O_6$, every molecule that is dissolved will represent one species added to the solution, For every sugar particle that is dissolved one particle goes into solution, and we have $i = 1$. The van't Hoff number of molecular substances that completely ionize in water equals the number of ions formed when one molecule dissolves. For ionic substances the van't Hoff number generally equals the number of ions formed when one empirical formula unit of a substance dissolves. Sodium sulfate Na_2SO_4 for example has a van't Hoff number of 3 since it forms three ions per formula unit when it dissolves in water. Substances that only partially ionize in water have non-integer van't Hoff numbers. In these cases, the van't Hoff number must be determined by experiment or from an equilibrium calculation. Acetic acid CH_3COOH for example has a van't Hoff number that depends on its concentration in solution. A 1.00 M_m solution of acetic acid has a van't Hoff number of 1.005. For every 1000 acetic acid molecules added to the solution 1005 particles result. 995 of the particles are acetic acid molecules, 5 are protons, and 5 are acetate ions.

12.3.0 Setting-up a cooling bath

The effect of freezing point depression investigated in this experiment is also used to set up a cooling bath. Put crushed ice in a layer 2-3cm deep in a 600 mL beaker. Sprinkle a thin layer of rock salt on top of the ice. Continue to alternate layers of ice and rock salt until the beaker is filled up to the 500 mL mark. Then stir the ice mixture. Insert a thermometer into the cooling bath and monitor its temperature. For this experiment, it is necessary that the temperature of the cooling bath stay below -10°C. Occasionally stir the contents of the cooling bath. Constantly monitor the temperature of the cooling bath, and if the temperature rises above this threshold value, replace some of the liquid with additional ice, and add more salt to the cooling bath.

12.3.1 The freezing point of water

Although it is well known that the freezing point of pure water at 1 atm pressure is 0.0C, the measured value depends on the current conditions as well as the experimental set-up and calibration. However, since this experiment is based on temperature differences rather than absolute temperatures, one still can obtain valuable results when taking the experimentally determined freezing point of water as point of reference.

Add a few grains of Ottawa sand to a 25 x 200mm test tube. Then using a volumetric pipet, add 20.0 mL of deionized water, measured to the nearest 0.05 mL. Insert the Accumet temperature probe into solution, making sure it does not touch the bottom of the test tube. Place the test tube in the ice bath and observe the temperature of the solution. When the temperature of the solution reaches about 5.0°C obtain a temperature reading for the time t = 0s and record temperature readings at 10-second intervals. Occasionally stir the solution during the cooling process. Continue recording until the solid-liquid equilibrium phase is reached and monitor temperature changes for another 2-3 minutes. It may be necessary to record temperature changes for up to 10 minutes to establish a good curve. Determine the freezing point of the water.

12.3.2 The freezing point depression constant of water

In a 25x200mm test tube, mix *exactly* 20.0 mL of deionized water with *exactly* 1.0 mL of methanol (CH_3OH). Use a volumetric pipet to dispense the deionized water and the provided graduated pipet to dispense the methanol. Record the volumes to the nearest 0.05 mL. Use the densities of water (1.00g/mL) and methanol (0.791g/mL) to get the masses of solvent and solute. Follow the procedure outlined in 12.3.1 above, and determine the freezing point of the solution.

12.3.3 The van't Hoff number of an inorganic salt

In a 25x200mm test tube, mix *exactly* 20.0 mL of deionized water with *approximately* 1.0g of potassium nitrate (KNO_3) Record the volumes to the nearest 0.05 mL, and the grams to the nearest mg. Use the room-temperature density of water (1.00 g/mL) to obtain the mass of the solvent. Follow the procedure outlined in 12.3.1 above, use the freezing point depression to determine the van't Hoff number of potassium nitrate at its current concentration.

12.4.0 Constructing cooling curves

For each of the set of data collected in sections 12.12.2, 12.3.3 and 12.3.4, construct a time-temperature plot of the cooling process, a **cooling curve**. Use a sheet of graph paper to plot the data; alternatively, you can use a spreadsheet program such as Excel to produce a cooling curve. An exemplarily cooling curve is shown in Figure 12-6.

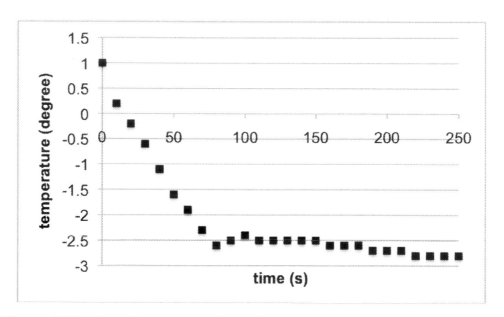

Figure 12-6: Time-Temperature data of a cooling process

In the time interval between 0 and 80 seconds, we see the initial cooling phase of the solution. At 100 seconds, we observe the onset of the liquid-solid equilibrium. The temperature now decreases very slowly. The freezing point is evaluated by extrapolation, and we estimate a freezing point of -2.4 °C

On occasion you might observe a region of supercooling, compare Figure 12.4. However, if a seed crystal is present, and if there is no build-up of a substantial temperature gradient during the cooling process, supercooling is prevented, and the freezing point manifests itself in a change of slope of time-temperature line.

If the transition from liquid to liquid-solid occurs without a sharp transition point and in a continuous fashion, construct straight-line plots for points that represent the cooling region of the liquid, and the cooling region of the liquid-solid equilibrium. An example plot is shown in Figure 12. 7. Select regions based on their cooling rates; for the initial cooling phase we observe a cooling rate of about 0.2°C/10s, whereas for the final cooling state the rate drops to about 0.1°C/20s The point where these two lines intercept represents the freezing point of the solution. Observe that the data set is partitioned into three groups; points that represent a transition phase are omitted from the construction of trend-lines. The R2-values indicate a satisfactory data fit, and from the intercept of the two trendlines we estimate a freezing point of -1.4 °C.

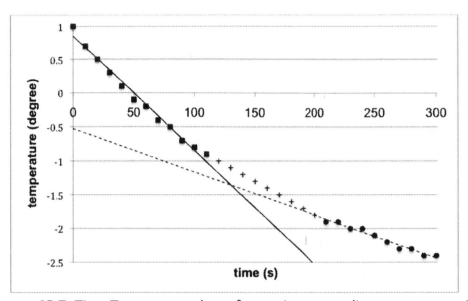

Figure 12-7: Time-Temperature data of a continuous cooling process, partitioned into an initial phase (▪), a transition region(+), and the final state (●).

If one follows such a partitioning approach, it is often necessary to provide the best fit equations for each region of data from each graph, as well as the R2 value for each line. An acceptable R^2 value is usually greater than 0.9.

12.4.1 The freezing point of water

Use the data collected in 12.3.1, construct a cooling curve and determine the freezing point of water. This can be determined from the intersection of the lines of the two regions of the graph. An exemplarily curve is depicted in Figure 12-8. Transition regions (areas of supercooling) are omitted from the graph. Report the best-fit equation and R^2 value for each region.

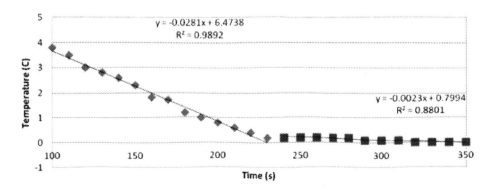

Figure 12-8: Determining the freezing point of a liquid.

12.4.2 The freezing point depression constant of water

Use the data collected in 12.3.2 to determine the freezing point depression constant K_f of water. Construct a cooling curve and determine the freezing point depression of the methanol solution. An exemplarily curve is depicted in Figure 12-9. Transition regions (areas of supercooling) are omitted from the graph. Report the best-fit equation and R^2 value for each region. The freezing point of the methanol solution can be determined from the intersection of the lines of the two regions of the graph.

From the volume of deionized water determine the mass of the solvent. From the volume of methanol determine the mass and determine the number of moles from its molecular weight. Calculate the Molality of the solution, and determine K_f of water.

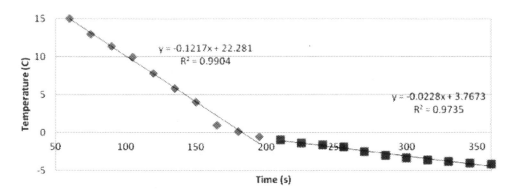

Figure 12-9: Determining the freezing point depression constant of a liquid.

12.4.3 The van't Hoff number of an inorganic salt

Use the data collected in 12.3.3, construct a cooling curve and determine the freezing point depression of the potassium nitrate solution. This can be obtained from the intersection of the lines of the two regions of the graph. An exemplarily curve is depicted in Figure 12-10. Transition regions (areas of supercooling) are omitted from the graph. Report the best-fit equation and R^2 value for each region.

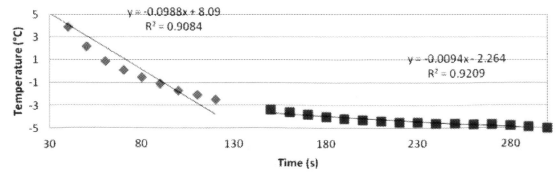

Figure 12-10: Determining the freezing point of a salt solution.

Use the freezing point depression ΔT_f together with the mass of the solvent to calculate a value for $i \cdot n_{solute}$. Use the mass of potassium nitrate and its molecular weight to calculate n_{solute}. Use this data to determine the van't Hoff number i of the inorganic salt.

EXPERIMENT 13: Chemical Kinetics I — the *Iodine Clock* Reaction

13.1. Purpose

In experiment 13, the reaction order and the rate constant of the *Iodine Clock* reaction will be established.

13.2. Background

One of the goals in a chemical kinetics study is to derive an equation that can be used to predict the relationship between the rate or the speed of a reaction and the concentration of the reactants. Such an experimentally determined relation is called a **rate law**, or **rate equation**.

If we consider a hypothetical reaction such as the one displayed in equation 13.1,

$$a \cdot A + b \cdot B + c \cdot C + \cdots \rightarrow products \tag{13.1}$$

then the *rate of the reaction* vr is often of the form as shown in equation 13.2:

$$v_r = k \cdot [A]^m \cdot [B]^n \cdot [C]^p \cdots \tag{13.2}$$

The characteristic proportionality constant k is called the **rate constant** of the reaction. The *kinetic exponents m, n, p* ... are generally small, positive whole numbers, although in some cases they may be zero, or fractions of two integer numbers. Note that the kinetic exponents are not related to the stoichiometric coefficients. Usually, $m \neq a$, $n \neq b$, and so on. The kinetic exponents define the *order* of a reaction. The reaction of equation 13.1 then is of order m in A, of order n in B, and of order p in C, and the *overall* **order of reaction** is the sum of the kinetic exponents.

A successful reaction is made up of three intertwined events: it depends on the reactants coming together, orientating and aligning themselves properly and having sufficient energy to complete the interaction to form product. In this lab experiment we will we will explore what roles the concentration of the reactants have on the rate of a particular reaction.

13.1.1 The Iodine Clock

The *Iodine Clock* reaction is a classical demonstration experiment to display chemical kinetics in action; it was discovered in 1886 by Landoldt. This reaction is also an example of a *chemical clock*; a mixture of reacting chemical compounds in which the concentration of one component shows an abrupt change accompanied by a visible color effect. In self-indicating reactions of this type, in which nothing seems to happen for while and then a change suddenly becomes visible, the onset of the color change may be used to time the reaction.

The iodine clock reaction exists in several variations. Common to all protocols is the oxidation of iodide anion to yield molecular iodine; the various reactions differ in the choice of the oxidizing agent. Persulfate, iodate, and chlorate may be employed, among other agents.

To make an Iodine clock work, we need to include two components, *detection* and *time delay*, which we now shall discuss in detail.

and *time delay*, which we now shall discuss in detail.

13.1.2 Detection in the Iodine Clock

In this experiment, we will explore the hydrogen peroxide variation of the *iodine Clock* reaction. This reaction starts from a solution of hydrogen peroxide with sulfuric acid which proceeds conveniently slow near room temperature, and which can be monitored easily by a change in color.

$$H_2O_2 + 2H^+ 2I^- \xrightarrow{slow} I_2 + 2H_2O \tag{13.3}$$

As this reaction proceeds, the colorless solution gradually develops a light orange color due to the product I_2. However, since the product iodine is also in equilibrium with additional iodide to produce triiodide anion I_3^-, the appearance of iodine is not easily noticed.

$$I_2 + I^- \longleftrightarrow I_3^- \tag{13.4}$$

But, since I_2 and I_3^- coexist in equilibrium, if we can clearly detect the presence of I_3^- then we can infer that this is the point where free I_2 has been generated. We use starch as indicator of the triiodide (I_3^-). Starch, a biopolymer of glucose, has a spiral structure, and the triiodide ion slips into the coil of the starch and forms a complex of intense dark-blue color (Figure 13-1).

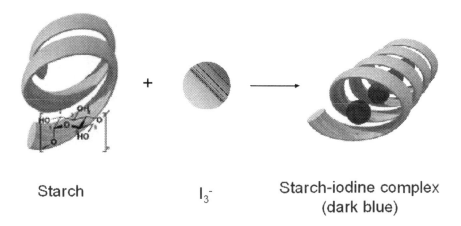

Starch I_3^- Starch-iodine complex
(dark blue)

Figure 13-1: Formation of the starch-iodine complex.

13.1.3 Time Delay in the Iodine Clock

Because of the difficulty of timing the appearance of the I_2, we will make use of another much faster reaction in the same solution to mark the progress of the slow reaction:

$$I_2 + 2S_2O_3^{2-} \xrightarrow{fast} 2I^- + 2H_2O + S_4O_6^{2-} \tag{13.5}$$

The oxidation of thiosulfate ($S_2O_3^{2-}$) is so fast that any free I_2 produced by oxidation with hydrogen peroxide (reaction 13.3) is instantly consumed by the thiosulfate (reaction 13.5) and converted back to 2I⁻, which then can follow reaction 13.3 once again.

This effectively forms a cycle of reactions (figure 13-2) where no free I_2 can develop as long as $S_2O_3^{2-}$ exists in solution, and therefore no I_3^- can develop. Because both $S_2O_3^{2-}$ and $S_4O_6^{2-}$ are colorless, the solution remains colorless.

However, this cycle only lasts as long as there is unconsumed $S_2O_3^{2-}$ in solution. We do not add enough thiosulfate to react with all the I_2 that will be formed from reaction 13.3 (while the I⁻ is regenerated during the cycle, the $S_2O_3^{2-}$ is eventually depleted). Eventually I_3^- will be able to form and then form the blue starch complex.

By this device the reaction solution stays colorless until the instant all the thiosulfate is consumed.

The amount of time it actually takes to consume the thiosulfate and end the cycle will depend on two factors: the original amount of thiosulfate in solution and the rate of reaction 13.3 (the slow reaction).

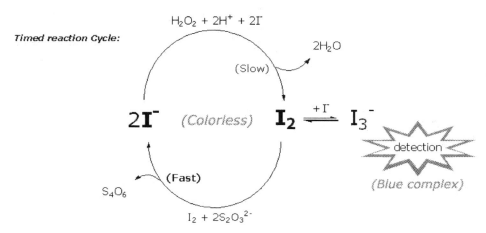

Figure 13-2: Timed reaction cycle for the Iodine clock, showing the cycle between reactions 13.3 and 13.5, with the eventual exhaustion of reaction 13.5 leading to reaction 13.4 and solution color change.

We time the reaction from the initial mixing until the appearance of I_2. Due to the presence of the starch indicator, the first appearance of I_2 causes a dramatic color change of the solution.

13.1.4 Rate law of the Iodine Clock

The rate law for the *Iodine Clock* reaction is derived from the slow reaction 13.3:

$$v_r = k \cdot [I^-]^m \cdot [H_2O_2]^n \cdot [H^+]^p \tag{13.6}$$

We can use the **method of initial rates** to determine the exponents and the rate constant of the rate-law expression of equation 4.6. The reaction is carried out with different initial concentrations of the various reactants, and the resultant changes in initial rates are analyzed. The *initial rate of a reaction* is the rate of a reaction immediately after the reactants are brought together, and it can be obtained from the concentration of a chosen reactant [A] at a point t_f as soon as possible after mixing. The point at which all reactants come together determines the initial time t_i.

$$v_r = -\frac{1}{a} \cdot \frac{d[A]}{dt} \approx -\frac{1}{a} \cdot \frac{\Delta[A]}{\Delta t} = -\frac{1}{a} \cdot \frac{[A]_{t=t_f} - [A]_{t=t_i}}{t_f - t_i} \tag{13.7}$$

In equation 13.7, a represents the stoichiometric coefficient of reactant A in the reaction of interest.

We use the progress of the fast reaction (equation 13.5), in order to determine changes in reactant concentration for the reaction of interest (equation 13.3). We already know the initial concentration of $S_2O_3^{2-}$ at time t_i and we will measure the time necessary for $S_2O_3^{2-}$ to be consumed, $[S_2O_3^{2-}]_{t=ti} = 0$. These quantities determine the rate of the slow reaction. The interplay between the fast and slow reaction is demonstrated for hydrogen peroxide H_2O_2, but a similar analysis can easily be obtained for the iodide anion I^- also.

Changes in thiosulfate and hydrogen peroxide concentration during the course of the *Iodine Clock* reaction are illustrated in Figure 13-3.

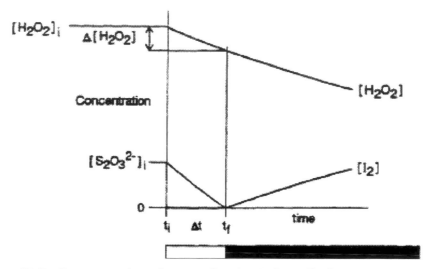

Figure 13-3: Concentration changes for the *Iodine Clock*.

The following changes occur between times t_i and t_f: The thiosulfate concentration drops from it initial value of $[S_2O_3^{2-}]_{t=ti}$ to zero. From equation 13.5, we ascertain the $\Delta[I_2]$ consumed is $\frac{1}{2}[S_2O_3^{2-}]_{t=ti}$. Further, the amount of I_2 consumed in the fast reaction 13.5 is equal to the amount of I_2 produced in the slow reaction 13.3. From equation 13.3, we can deduce that for each I_2 mole produced, one mole of H_2O_2 is consumed. This leads to the following expression for the initial rate of the reaction:

$$v_r = -\frac{\Delta[H_2O_2]}{\Delta t} = -\frac{1}{2}\frac{\Delta[S_2O_3^{2-}]}{\Delta t} = -\frac{1}{2}\frac{[S_2O_3^{2-}]_{t=t_f} - [S_2O_3^{2-}]_{t=t_i}}{t_f - t_i} =$$

$$-\frac{1}{2}\frac{0 - [S_2O_3^{2-}]_{t=t_i}}{t_f - 0} = \frac{1}{2}\frac{[S_2O_3^{2-}]_{t=t_i}}{t_f} \tag{13.8}$$

Thus, the rate of the reaction can be determined from the initial concentration of thiosulfate and the time elapsed until the blue color appeared.

13.3. Procedure

The reactants will be introduced by way of burets; make sure that you accurately measure out of proper amount of reactants. The following reactant stock solutions with the appropriate concentrations are needed for the experiment, which will be provided, or which you have to prepare before you begin your kinetic experiments:

H_2SO_4: 0.050 M (sulfuric acid)

KI: 0.100 M (potassium iodide)

$Na_2S_2O_3$: 0.100 M (sodium thiosulfate)

H_2O_2: 0.500 M (hydrogen peroxide)

K_2SO_4: 0.100 M (potassium sulfate)

You will carry out seven trials of the *Iodine Clock* reaction, which will use different initial concentrations of reactants.

In the following, a general protocol for the reaction is outlined:

1. Fill a *clean* 18×150 test tube with the appropriate amount of H_2SO_4, KI, $Na_2S_2O_3$ and K_2SO_4 solutions. Vigorously swirl and mix the contents of the test tube.

2. Add 1.0 ml of starch solution to the reaction mixture, and swirl the solution.

3. In a separate test tube measure out the proper amount of hydrogen peroxide. As soon as the H_2O_2 is mixed with the solution from step 1, the reaction starts.

4. Quickly add the proper amount of hydrogen peroxide solution to the other combined solution, and immediately start the timer.

5. Vigorously swirl and mix the contents of the test tube.

6. As soon as a blue color is detected, stop the timer. Report the reaction time in your lab note book.

Set up the following table in your lab note book, in which you will collect your results for the different trials:

Trial	H_2O_2	KI	H_2SO_4	$Na_2S_2O_3$	K_2SO_4	Starch	t (s)
#1	2.0 ml	1.0 ml	1.0 ml	1.0 ml	4.0 ml	1.0 ml	
#2	2.0 ml	1.0 ml	2.0 ml	1.0 ml	3.0 ml	1.0 ml	
#3	4.0 ml	1.0 ml	1.0 ml	1.0 ml	2.0 ml	1.0 ml	
#4	2.0 ml	2.0 ml	1.0 ml	1.0 ml	3.0 ml	1.0 ml	
#5	2.0 ml	1.0 ml	3.0 ml	1.0 ml	2.0 ml	1.0 ml	
#6	3.0 ml	1.0 ml	1.0 ml	1.0 ml	3.0 ml	1.0 ml	
#7	2.0 ml	3.0 ml	1.0 ml	1.0 ml	2.0 ml	1.0 ml	

All trial solutions are brought to a same reaction volume of 10 ml. Instead of adding de-ionized water, a sodium sulfate solution is used in order to keep the ion strength of the different solutions at approximately the same level.

13.4. Calculations

Before you begin calculating kinetic exponents and rate constants, set up the following table and complete all entries. The table will serve as a database for further calculations:

Trial	$[H^+]_{init}$	$[I^-]_{init}$	$[H_2O_2]_{init}$	$[S_2O_3^{2-}]init$	initial rate v (in M/s)
#1					
#2					
#3					
#4					
#5					
#6					
#7					

Calculate the initial concentrations from volume and concentration of the respective stock solutions:

$$c_{init} = \frac{c_{stock} \times V_{stock}}{V_{total}} = c_{stock} \times \frac{V_{stock}}{10.0\,ml}$$

Although sulfuric acid is a diprotic acid, only the first proton dissociates completely, and a valid approximation for the concentration of hydronium ions is $[H^+] \approx [H_2SO_4]$.

Base your calculation of the initial rates v on the change in thiosulfate concentration as outlined in equation 13.8.

Calculate the **reaction order exponents** by taking the ratio of the rate equations for two trials that differ only in the initial concentration of one reactant.

$$\frac{v_1}{v_2} = \frac{k \cdot [I^-]_1^m \cdot [H_2O_2]_1^n \cdot [H^+]_1^p}{k \cdot [I^-]_2^m \cdot [H_2O_2]_2^n \cdot [H^+]_2^p}$$

An exemplarily calculation is given below. If trials #1 and #2 resulted in reaction times of 95s and 45s, we would get:

$$\frac{trial\ \#2}{trial\ \#1}: \quad \frac{1.11 \times 10^{-4}}{5.26 \times 10^{-5}} = \frac{k \cdot (0.010)^m \cdot (0.200)^n \cdot (0.100)^p}{k \cdot (0.010)^m \cdot (0.100)^n \cdot (0.100)^p}$$

$$\Rightarrow \quad 2.11 = 2^n$$

Remember that the k-value is the same in both reactions, and that all equal terms will divide out to 1.

By inspection, it follows that n is approximately 1. We can formally solve this equation by taking logarithms of both sides of the equation (either ln or log):

$$\log 2.11 = \log 2^n = n \cdot \log 2$$

$$\Rightarrow \quad n = \frac{\log 2.11}{\log 2} = \frac{0.324}{0.301} = 1.08 \approx 1$$

Since *kinetic exponents* are generally small, positive whole numbers, fractions of two integer numbers or zero, it is permissible to round off the kinetic exponents to the nearest small integer, ratio of two small integers (e.g. ½ = 0.5) or zero.

For each of the seven trials, calculate a value for k from equation 13.6. Use the initial rate, the initial concentration, and the kinetic exponents.

Also calculate an average rate constant $\bar{k}$ and its standard deviation.

Use a table to summarize your results. The checkmarks indicate the trials that you have used to calculate a particular kinetic exponent. For each trial calculate a value for the rate constant k:

	#1	#2	#3	#4	#5	#6	#7	
m_r	✓	–	–	✓	–	–	–	$m =$
m_r	✓	–	–	–	–	–	✓	$m =$
$n_{H_2O_2}$	✓	–	✓	–	–	–	–	$n =$
$n_{H_2O_2}$	✓	–	–	–	–	✓	–	$n =$
p_{H^+}	✓	✓	–	–	–	–	–	$P =$
p_{H^+}	✓	–	–	–	✓	–	–	$P =$
k								$\bar{k} =$

13.5. Discussion

Discuss the gist of your results, and comment on the precision of the experimental procedure employed in experiment 13. Include the average rate constant and its standard deviation in your discussion.

The following reaction mechanism is proposed for the *Iodine Clock* reaction:

    I. $H_2O_2 + I^- \rightarrow I\cdot + \cdot OH + OH^-$

    II. $\cdot OH + I^- \rightarrow I\cdot + OH^-$

    III. $I\cdot + I\cdot \rightarrow I_2$

    IV. $2\{OH^- + H^+ \rightarrow H_2O\}$

Show that this mechanism is consistent with the stoichiometry of the reaction.

EXPERIMENT 14: Chemical Equilibrium — Complex Ion Formation

14.1 Purpose

In experiment 14, we will determine the equilibrium constant for the formation of a transition metal complex ion.

14.2 Background

Many transition metal ions form **complex ions**, which are composed of a central metal cation to which other groups called *ligands* are bonded. Ligands can either be ionic species, typically anions, or neutral molecules, such as water or ammonia. Substances containing complex ions are generally as **coordination compounds**.

Since many transition metal complexes have a distinctive color, the concentration of transition metal complexes can easily be determined by using spectrophotometric measurements.

The iron(III) cation forms a complex with the thiocyanate anion SCN^- that is of deep blood-red color. Thiocyanate is used in photographic processes, and the iron(III)thiocyanoto complex $\{Fe(SCN)\}^{2+}$ is often used to determine the concentration of thiocyanate solutions. The chemical equation for the complex forming reaction is shown in equation 14.1:

$$Fe^{3+} + SCN^- \;\rightleftharpoons\; \{Fe(SCN)\}^{2+} \tag{14.1}$$

The reaction of equation 5.1 represents a **chemical equilibrium**, and the corresponding *equilibrium constant* K_c is defined in equation 14.2:

$$K_C = \frac{[\{Fe(SCN)\}^{2+}]}{[Fe^{3+}][SCN^-]} \tag{14.2}$$

However, a few complications arise when measuring the equilibrium constant for the complex forming reaction of equation 14.1. When an iron(III) salt, such as $Fe(NO_3)_3$, is dissolved in water, the iron(III) cation forms a hexaquo complex $\{Fe(H_2O)_6\}^{3+}$. This complex is acidic in nature, and eventually leads to the formation of insoluble iron(III) hydroxide, equation 14.3.

$$
\begin{aligned}
\{Fe(H_2O)_6\}^{3+} &\rightleftharpoons \{Fe(OH)(H_2O)_5\}^{2+} + H^+ \\
\{Fe(OH)(H_2O)_5\}^{2+} &\rightleftharpoons \{Fe(OH)_2(H_2O)_4\}^+ + H^+ \\
\{Fe(OH)_2(H_2O)_4\}^+ &\rightleftharpoons Fe(OH)_3\!\downarrow + 3\,H_2O + H^+
\end{aligned}
\tag{14.3}
$$

The chemical reactions outlined in equation 14.3 would strongly influence the concentration of free iron(III) cation. In order to prevent the precipitation of insoluble iron(III)hydroxide, the formation of the iron(III)thiocyanoto complex is carried out in acidic solution. The presence of an acid shifts the equilibria of equation 14.3 to the left, thus preventing the formation of any hydroxide complexes. Ideally, the acid employed has the same conjugated-base anion as the iron salt used. Since in this experiment a solution of iron(III) nitrate is used, nitric acid HNO_3 is the acid of choice.

The acidic conditions have a second beneficial effect. Iron(III) cation can form a complex with more than one thiocyanato ligand, as shown in equation 14.4:

$$Fe^{3+} + n\ SCN^- \rightarrow \{Fe(SCN)_n\}^{(3-n)+} \quad n \geq 1 \tag{14.4}$$

However, under acidic conditions, the complex formation is limited to the monothiocyanato complex $\{Fe(SCN)\}^{2+}$ (n = 1).

A second problem arises in the construction of Beer's law plot. Since the formation of the iron(iii) thiocyanato complex is an equilibrium process, it does not proceed to completion. Thus, the concentration of the species involved in complex formation is not known *a priori*. Once again, the corresponding equilibrium will be accordingly shifted by employing LeChatelier's principle. When preparing solutions for Beer's Law plot, a limited quantity of Fe (III) ion is added to a large excess of SCN⁻ ion. By virtue of the large concentration of thiocyanate, nearly all of the Fe (III) ions will form the complex and the number of moles of complex formed will essentially be equal to the number of moles of iron (III) used to prepare the solution.

When calculating the equilibrium constant K_{eq} according to equation 14.2, we need not only the concentration of the iron(III) thiocyanato complex, but also the concentration of free iron(III) cation and free thiocyanato anion. We can calculate these concentrations by employing the principle of conservation of mass. It follows from equation 14.1 that for each mole of complex formed, one mole each of iron(III) cation and thiocyanato anion are used. Since the initial numbers of moles of Fe^{3+} and SCN⁻ are known, and since the number of moles of complex can be measured, we can employ the following relationships to obtain the number of moles of all species at equilibrium:

$$n(complex)_{eq} = n(complex)_{measured}$$

$$n(Fe^{3+})_{eq} = n(Fe^{3+})_{initial} - n(complex)_{eq}$$

$$n(SCN^-)_{eq} = n(SCN^-)_{initial} - n(complex)_{eq}$$

Furthermore, since all reaction volumes and initial volumes are known, the equilibrium concentrations are easily calculated.

14.3 Procedure

The following stock solutions will be used in the experiment:

    1) 0.5mM aqueous solution of iron(III)nitrate, $Fe(NO_3)_3$

    2) 2.5mM aqueous solution of iron(III)nitrate, $Fe(NO_3)_3$

    3) 1.0M aqueous solution of potassium thiocyanate, KSCN

    4) 2.5mM aqueous solution of potassium thiocyanate, KSCN

5) 0.1M aqueous solution of nitric acid, HNO_3

Make sure that for each experiment, you use the *correct solutions in the required concentrations!* Properly label your test tubes in which you will prepare solutions of different concentrations.

14.3.1 Calibration of the instrument

Absorptions are measured with a single-beam spectrophotometer, and the following instructions refer to the S42669PKND Fisher Educational Spectrophotometer. The general principles outlined apply to other spectrophotometers, such as the SPEC20, as well.

The instrument needs to be calibrated for measurements at a wavelength of 440 nm. The procedure described below is termed *blanking.* Blanking must be done each time a new wavelength is selected. The step-by-step procedure for setting up the spectrophotometer is as follows:

1. Turn on the spectrophotometer, and in order to stabilize the lamp and detector, allow the instrument to warm up for at least 15 minutes.

2. Push the %T/A selector to choose the A (Absorbance) operating mode.

3. Turn the wavelength control knob to 440nm.

4. Move the second order filter lever position to the appropriate filter setting. For measurements at 440nm, adjust the second order filter lever so that the dark-blue/black dot shows.

5. Fill a cuvette with blanking solution. Here, we use de-ionized water as blanking solution. If you use a 1 cm square cuvette, fill the cuvette almost completely, and insert the cuvette into the cuvette holder. Make sure you position the cuvette correctly in the cuvette holder, so that the light beam enters and leaves the cuvette through its clear and plain faces. Place the cuvette holder into the sample compartment. Be sure that the cuvette holder has been firmly pressed into the sample compartment and the lid of the sample compartment has been closed. If you use a tubular test tube cuvette, fill the cuvette 2/3 full with blanking solution. Place the test tube cuvette into the sample compartment. Be sure that the test tube cuvette has been firmly pressed into the sample compartment and the lid of the sample compartment has been closed.

6. Adjust the display to 0.00A by turning the 100%T/0A control.

7. Remove the cuvette from the sample compartment.

14.3.2 Calibration curve for complex concentration

Obtain five clean and dry test tubes, and prepare the following iron(III)thiocyanato complex solutions of different concentration by adding to the test-tubes:

i)   1ml of 0.5mM $Fe(NO_3)_3$, 5ml of 1.0M KSCN, 6ml of 0.1M HNO_3

ii) 2ml of 0.5mM $Fe(NO_3)_3$, 5ml of 1.0M KSCN, 5ml of 0.1M HNO_3

iii) 3ml of 0.5mM $Fe(NO_3)_3$, 5ml of 1.0M KSCN, 4ml of 0.1M HNO_3

iv) 4ml of 0.5mM $Fe(NO_3)_3$, 4ml of 1.0M KSCN, 4ml of 0.1M HNO_3

v)   5ml of 0.5mM $Fe(NO_3)_3$, 4ml of 1.0M KSCN, 3ml of 0.1M HNO_3

Gently shake or stir the test tubes in order to mix the reaction solution. Wait about 5 minutes after mixing before you measure the absorbance of the five solutions.

For each of the five complex solutions, rinse a 1cm cuvette with approximately 0.5 to 1ml of the complex solution. Then fill the cuvette with the complex solution, and obtain an absorbance reading with the spectrophotometer. Use a Pasteur-pipette when charging the cuvette with complex solution.

14.3.3 Determination of the equilibrium constant

Obtain five clean and dry test tubes, and prepare the following equilibrium solutions by adding to the test-tubes:

i) 1ml of 2.5mM $Fe(NO_3)_3$, 1ml of 2.5mM KSCN, 5ml of 0.1M HNO_3

ii) 1ml of 2.5mM $Fe(NO_3)_3$, 3ml of 2.5mM KSCN, 3ml of 0.1M HNO_3

iii) 2ml of 2.5mM $Fe(NO_3)_3$, 1ml of 2.5mM KSCN, 4ml of 0.1M HNO_3

iv) 2ml of 2.5mM $Fe(NO_3)_3$, 2ml of 2.5mM KSCN, 3ml of 0.1M HNO_3

v) 2ml of 2.5mM $Fe(NO_3)_3$, 3ml of 2.5mM KSCN, 5ml of 0.1M HNO_3

Gently shake or stir the test tubes in order to mix the reaction solution. Wait about 5 minutes after mixing before you measure the absorbance of the five solutions.

For each of the five complex solutions, rinse a 1cm cuvette with approximately 0.5 to 1ml of the complex solution. Then fill the cuvette with the complex solution, and obtain an absorbance reading with the spectrophotometer. Use a Pasteur-pipette when charging the cuvette with complex solution.

All extra solution and chemical waste is to be properly disposed of in the appropriate waste containers placed in the fume hood.

14.4 Calculations

14.4.1 Beer's Law plot

For the calibration curve, calculate the concentrations of the ${Fe(SCN)}^{2+}$ solutions of test tubes 1 to 5. Set up a concentration-absorbance table:

Test Tube #	Concentration	Absorbance
1		
2		
3		
4		
5		

Assume that under the given reaction conditions all of the iron(III) cation is converted into the final complex when calculating the concentration of the iron(III)thiocyanato complex. Thus, $[{Fe(SCN)}^{2+}]_{final} = [Fe(NO_3)_3]_{initial}$.

Use a spreadsheet program such as Excel to construct an absorbance-concentration plot (compare Experiment 10). Fit a trendline to your set of data, and set the intercept at zero. Record the equation of the trendline. Include a print-out of your plot as part of your lab-report.

From the slope of your trendline, obtain values for $1/(\varepsilon \cdot l)$ and for the molar absorptivity coefficient ε. Assume a length of 1cm for the cuvette you have used. Report the values of $1/(\varepsilon \cdot l)$ and ε with the *correct units*.

14.4.2 Calculation of the equilibrium constant

Use the Lambert-Beer law, the value for $1/(\varepsilon \cdot l)$ calculated in section 14.4.1, and the initial concentrations of the reagents, to calculate the concentrations of all species at equilibrium for the five different reaction solutions investigated in section 14.3.3.

Use an *ICE* table to calculate the required concentrations. In the *ICE* table shown below, the known experimental values are indicated in **bold**:

	Fe^{3+}	SCN^-	$\{Fe(SCN)\}^{2+}$
I	$\mathbf{c(Fe^{3+})_{initial}}$	$\mathbf{c(SCN^-)_{initial}}$	**0**
C	-x	-x	+x
E	$c(Fe^{3+})_{initial}$ - x	$c(SCN^-)_{initial}$ - x	$\mathbf{c(\{Fe(SCN)\}^{2+})_{equilibrium}}$

For each of the different reaction solutions, calculate a value for K_c. Report an average value for the equilibrium constant $\bar{K}_c$ and report its standard deviation.

14.5 Discussion

Comment on the accuracy as well as the precision of the experimental procedure employed in experiment 14. Discuss possible sources of systematic errors and random errors.

EXPERIMENT 15: Acid-Base Chemistry III — Titration Curves

15.1 Purpose

In experiment 15, we will determine concentrations of various acidic solutions, as well as a value for the acid ionization constant K_a of a weak acid.

15.2 Background

Titration is a general class of experiments where a known property of one solution is used to infer an unknown property of another solution. In a titration, a **titrant** is added in controlled fashion to a solution of unknown properties through a buret. In acid-base chemistry, titration is often used to determine the **pH** and the **concentration** of a certain solution.

A **titration curve** can be drawn by plotting data obtained during a titration. Typically, titrant volume is entered on the x-axis, and pH on the y-axis. The titration curve is used to profile the unknown solution. The shape of the curve reveals characteristic properties of the acid or base that is titrated.

The titration of a strong acid with a strong base produces the following titration curve depicted in Figure 15-1.

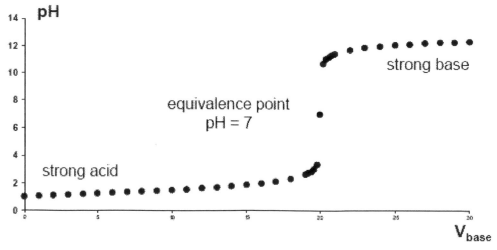

Figure 15-1: Titration curve for the titration of a strong acid with a strong base

Characteristic of the above curve is the sharp transition region near the equivalence point. The equivalence point for a strong acid-strong base titration curve is exactly at pH = 7 because the salt produced does not undergo any hydrolysis reactions.

However, if a strong base is used to titrate a weak acid, the pH at the equivalence point will not be 7. A lag will occur in reaching the equivalence point, as some of the weak acid is converted to its conjugate base. The pair of a weak acid and its conjugate base comprises a **buffer**, and the resultant lag preceding the equivalence point, is called the **buffer region**. The titration curve for such a titration is schematically shown in Figure 15-2.

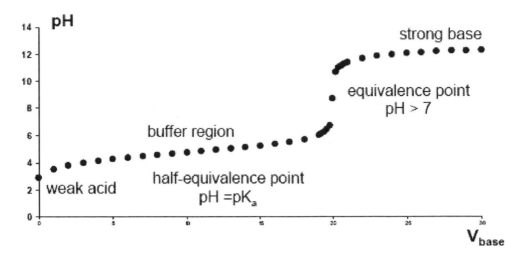

Figure 15-2: Titration curve for the titration of a weak acid with a strong base

In the buffering region, it takes a large amount of base to produce a small change in the pH of the receiving solution. Also, because the conjugate base is basic, as its name implies, the pH will be greater than 7 at the equivalence point.

Characteristic for both titrations curves discussed above is the **equivalence point**, the condition in which the reactants are stoichiometric proportions. They consume each other, and neither reactant is in excess. Thus, for the number of moles n the following condition holds true (equation 15.1):

$$n_{acid}^{initially\ present} = n_{base}^{added} \qquad \textbf{(15.1)}$$

If the initial volume of the acid solution, and the volume and concentration of the base added are known, the concentration of the acid can be determined (equation 15.2).

$$c_{acid} = c_{base}^{added} \cdot \frac{V_{base}^{added}}{V_{acid}^{initial}} \qquad \textbf{(15.2)}$$

When talking about the titration of a weak acid, one should not confuse the *base added* during the titration, e.g. the titrant, with the *conjugate base formed* during the titration. This is exemplarily illustrated in Scheme 15-1 for the titration of acidic acid CH_3COOH, for short AcOH.

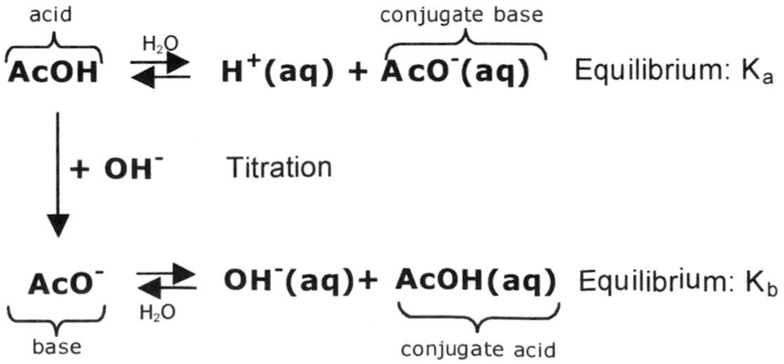

acid   conjugate base

AcOH $\underset{H_2O}{\rightleftarrows}$ **H$^+$(aq) + AcO$^-$(aq)**   Equilibrium: K_a

$\downarrow$ **+ OH$^-$**   Titration

AcO$^-$ $\underset{H_2O}{\rightleftarrows}$ **OH$^-$(aq)+ AcOH(aq)**   Equilibrium: K_b

base   conjugate acid

Scheme 15-1

The general equation that governs buffer solutions is the **Henderson-Hasselbach equation**, equation 15.3:

$$pH = pK_a + \log \frac{[conjugate\ base]}{[acid]}$$

(15.3)

When the concentrations of acid and conjugate base are equal, equation 15.3 reduces to the following simple expression (equation 15.4):

$$pH^{half-equivalence} = pK_a$$

(15.4)

Thus, the titration curve should also contain information about the acid ionization constant Ka. The point during a titration at which exactly half of the amount of titrant is added to reach the equivalence point is called the **half-equivalence point**. At this point, half of the amount of acid initially present is converted into its conjugate base. Although the concentration of acid and conjugate base is further determined by the corresponding acid and base equilibria, it is fair to approximate that at the half-equivalence point the concentration of the weak acid is equal to the concentration of its conjugate base. Therefore, the pH at the half-equivalence point is equal to the pKa value of the weak acid titrated (compare Figure 15-2).

15.3 Procedure

The pH values will be measured with the use of the accumet® AB15 pH/mV/°C Meter. The instrument should be operated in pH-measure mode, and the "Measure" window should display "pH", rather than "mV" or "REL mV". If the instrument is not set to pH, press and release the <u>mode</u> key until the digital display indicates pH mode.

To prepare the pH electrode for measurements, carefully remove the electrode from its protective storage solution. Thoroughly rinse the lower section of the probe, especially the region of the bulb, using de-ionized water. The electrodes are sensitive instruments, and suffer irreversible damage when drying out *Rinse the tip of the electrode with de-ionized water, and slide the electrode back into the protective storage solution after each series of measurements.*

15.3.1 Calibrating the pH sensor

The pH-sensor is calibrated by immersion into commercially available standard pH solutions. The probe used in experiment 15 requires at least a two-point calibration, and since a weak acid will be titrated, the pH values chosen for calibration are in the slightly acidic region (pH = 4), and the neutral region (pH = 7). Additionally, a third calibration point might be added, using a buffer solution in the basic regime (pH = 10).

The instrument is constructed for auto buffer recognition, and three different buffer groups can be used. The three buffer groups are US buffers (pH = 2;4;7;10;12), European buffers (pH = 1;3;6;8;10;13) and NIST buffers (pH = 1.68;4.01;6.86;9.18;12.46). Standard buffers chosen for this experiment are from the set of US buffers, and the instrument should be setup for US buffers recognition. To check the correct buffer group selection, access the "pH Buffer Group" menu from the pH Measure screen by pressing the <u>setup</u> key. The screen will display the "BUFFER select" icon and a series of numbers corresponding to the buffer group chosen (2;4;7;10;12 in case of US buffers). If the instrument displays values for the US buffer group, press enter to return to the "Measure" screen. Otherwise, continue to press setup until the desired buffer group is displayed, and then enter to accept the buffer group and return to the "Measure" screen.

Since the calibration of the instrument is highly dependent on the external conditions under which the instrument is used, the instrument should be calibrated before any pH measurement is performed.

Obtain two 50mL beakers, rinse them with de-ionized water, and add about 20-30 mL of standard buffer solutions for pH=4, and pH=7, respectively. If a three-point calibration is required, get an additional beaker containing buffer solution for pH=10. Then, proceed with the following steps:

1. Press the <u>setup</u> key twice and the press <u>enter</u> to clear an existing standardization.

2. Rinse the electrode with de-ionized water. Immerse the electrode into a buffer from the selected group (e.g. pH=4 or pH=7). Stir or swirl moderately.

3. Press <u>std</u> to access the "Standardize" mode. The selected buffer group is displayed briefly.

4. Wait for the reading to stabilize.

5. Press <u>std</u> again to initiate standardization. The meter will automatically recognize the buffer and then return to the "Measure" screen.

6. Repeat steps 2-5 with a second buffer solution from the selected buffer group.

7. When the meter accepts the second buffer, it will briefly display the percent slope associated with the electrode's performance prior to returning to the "Measure" mode. Ideally, the slope of the calibration line will be 1 or 100%. Any electrode that produces a slope within the range of 0.90-1.02 or 90-102% will result in acceptable pH values, and the "GOOD ELECTRODE" message will appear.

8. If the electrode is outside this range, the meter will display "ELECTRODE ERROR", and will not return to the "Measure" screen until <u>enter</u> is pressed.

9. If you receive an "ELECTRODE ERROR" message, check your experimental set-up, clean your electrode with de-ionized water, and start over. If the problem persists, change the pH electrode.

10. If required, repeat steps 2-5 with a third buffer solution from the selected buffer group.

15.3.2 Determining the Equivalence Point

Before performing a precise pH-based titration, it is helpful to determine the volume of titrant required to reach the equivalence point by means of an indicator-based titration.

Rinse a 50ml buret with a few ml of titrant solution, in this case 0.1M NaOH, fill the buret with titrant solution, and allow a small amount of titrant to drain from the buret to ensure that the tip of the buret is properly filled with liquid. Take an initial volume reading and record the value $V_{initial}$ in your lab notebook.

Next, pipette a 25.00 ml aliquot of an acid solution of unknown concentration into a clean and dry 250 ml Erlenmeyer flask, and add about 100ml of de-ionized water. Add a few drops of phenolphtalein indicator to the acidic solution.

While constantly swirling the beaker containing the acidic solution, allow titrant from the buret to enter the beaker, in a slow, but constant flow. As soon as a faint pink color is observable, stop the constant-flow titration.

Continue the titration drop by drop. When the solution remains light pink and the color no longer fades, the endpoint of the titration is reached. Stop the titration, and record the volume V_{final} in your lab notebook.

The volume required to reach the equivalence point of the titration, $V_{equivalence}$, is obtained as the difference between the final volume V_{final} and the initial volume $V_{initial}$.

15.3.3 Recording a titration curve

Refill the 50 ml buret used in section 15.3.2 with titrant solution, in this case 0.1M NaOH. Make an initial volume reading and record the value $V_{initial}$ in your lab notebook. Next, pipette a 25.00 ml aliquot of an acid solution of unknown concentration into a clean and dry 150 ml beaker. Immerse the pH probe into the acid solution, swirl the solution, and after stabilization of the pH output, record the initial pH value in your lab notebook.

You will now add a volume V_{buff} of the NaOH titrant to the acid solution in about 8-10 aliquots of about 2.5-3.0 ml. This volume is calculated as follows: $V_{buff} = V_{equivalence}$ -1.5ml. After each addition of titrant, swirl the solution, and once the pH reading is stable, record the pH value in your lab notebook.

Next, 15 aliquots of 0.2ml NaOH are added to the reaction solution. After each addition of titrant, swirl the solution, and once the pH reading is stable, record pH value in your lab notebook.

Finally, 6 more aliquots of 2.5 ml NaOH are added to the reaction solution. After each addition of titrant, swirl the solution, and once the pH reading is stable, record pH value in your lab notebook.

Record the titration curve data in your lab notebook in form of a table as exemplarily shown below:

Buret Reading	Total Volume Added (ml)	pH Reading
0.45	0	1.03
2.95	2.50	1.03
5.80	5.35	1.05

15.3.4 Titration of a strong acid

Proceed with the steps described in section 15.3.2 and 15.3.3 for a solution of unknown concentration of a strong acid, here hydrochloric acid HCl.

15.3.5 Titration of a weak acid

Proceed with the steps described in section 15.3.2 and 15.3.3 for a solution of unknown concentration of a weak acid, here acetic acid CH_3COOH.

15.4 Calculations

15.4.1 Indicator-based titration

For each of the acid solutions investigated in this experiment, determine the concentration from the data collected according to the procedure in section 15.3.2. Base your calculations on equation 15.2.

15.4.2 Titration curves

For each of the unknown acids, construct a titration curve by plotting the data collected according to the procedure in section 15.3.3. You can use either a computer program to generate the titration curve, or construct the titration curve manually on a sheet of 1mm grid paper.

The equivalence points of the titration curves are then obtained by means of a geometric construction. With a compass, fit a circle into the transition regions before and after the equivalence point for a given titration curve. Connect the midpoints of the two circles by a straight line. The intercept between the straight line connecting the midpoints and the titration curve corresponds to the equivalence point of the titration. The steps of this procedure are schematically outlined in Figure 15-3.

Use the equivalence points obtained from the titration curves and calculate the concentration of the strong acid and the weak acid, respectively.

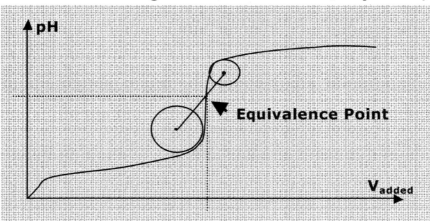

Figure 15-3: Geometric construction of the equivalence point

Include the titration curves showing the construction of the equivalence point as part of your lab report.

15.4.3 Ionization constant of acetic acid

Use the titration curve of acetic acid, and derive a value for K_a. Compare your value to the established literature value (consult your "General Chemistry" textbook).

15.5 Discussion

In your discussion, compare the concentrations obtained from indicator-titration and pH-titration. Comment on the accuracy of the different methods employed. Also, comment on how well your experiment reproduces the experimentally accepted value for K_a, and report the %error.

EXPERIMENT 16: Thermodynamics of Solution

16.1 Purpose

In experiment 16, we will determine values for enthalpy and entropy of solution of an inorganic salt, based on the temperature dependence of its solubility product K_{SP}.

16.2 Background

To understand why things dissolve at all, it is helpful to look at the solution formation process from a thermodynamic point of view. We therefore begin by considering a thermodynamic cycle representing the formation of a solution from the isolated solute and isolated solvent, as outlined in Figure 16-1.

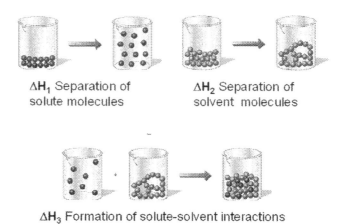

ΔH_1 Separation of solute molecules

ΔH_2 Separation of solvent molecules

ΔH_3 Formation of solute-solvent interactions

Figure 16-1: Break-down of the solution process into individual steps

The three distinct steps that we consider in solution formation are separation of solute molecules, separation of solvent molecules, and formation of solute-solvent interactions. Each step is associated with a change in enthalpy, $\Delta H1$, ΔH_2 and ΔH_3, respectively.

ΔH_1 and ΔH_2 are both positive because it requires energy to pull molecules or ions away from each other. This energy cost is due to the intermolecular forces present within any solute or solvent, such as electrostatic forces, dipole-dipole interactions, and hydrogen bonding. Each of these forces increases with decreasing distance. Therefore, it costs energy to pull molecules and ions away from each other. When the expanded form of the solvent and the solute are combined to form a solution, energy is released, causing ΔH_3 to be negative. This is due to the solute and solvent now interacting with each other through the various types of intermolecular forces.

According to **Hess' Law of Constant Heat Summation** we can express the energy **enthalpy of solution** $\Delta Hsol$ as follows (equation 16.1):

$$\Delta H_{sol} = \Delta H_1 + \Delta H_2 + \Delta H_3$$

$$(16.1)$$

Hess' Law is illustrated in Figure 16-2 for an exothermic and for an endothermic solution process.

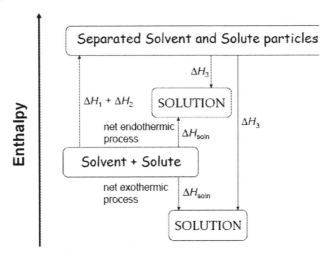

Figure 16-2: Illustration of Hess' Law for a solution formation process.

What determines the enthalpy of solution ΔH_{sol} is, therefore, the difference between the energy required to separate the solvent and solute and energy released when the separated solvent and solute form a solution. To restate this in simpler terms, solutions will form when the energy of interaction between the solvent and solute is greater than the sum of the solvent-solvent and solute-solute interactions.

In order to decide if a solution process constitutes a spontaneous reaction, we have to consider the change in free energy, ΔG, since for a spontaneous process at constant temperature and pressure, $\Delta G < 0$. The Gibbs equation describes how changes in free energy ΔG can be obtained from changes in enthalpy ΔH and entropy ΔS, equation 16.2.

$$\Delta G^0 = \Delta H^0 - T \cdot \Delta S^0 \qquad \textbf{(16.2)}$$

The spontaneous dispersal of energy associated with the solution formation process is its essential driving force. In fact, most compounds that are soluble in water have positive enthalpies of solution ΔH_{sol}. Therefore, from the equation 16.2 it would be predicted that the solubility of every compound should increase with increasing temperature. This prediction turns out to be correct for nearly every solvent and solute, with a few notable exceptions, such as sodium sulfate Na_2SO_4 in water or cerium sulfate $Ce_2(SO_4)_3$ in water. The fact that solubility decreases with increasing temperature, in these cases, is usually due to negative entropy of solution.

Knowledge of the free energy ΔG not only allows us to make a prediction whether a certain reaction is a spontaneous process, but it also contains information about the chemical equilibrium (equation 16.3.)

$$\Delta G^0 = -R \cdot T \cdot \ln K_{eq} \qquad \textbf{(16.3.)}$$

Here, K_{eq} is the equilibrium constant for a given chemical equilibrium. Combining and rearranging equations 16.2 and 16.3 yields the following expression for the equilibrium constant K (equation 16.4):

$$\ln K_{eq} = -\Delta H^0/(R \cdot T) + \Delta S^0/R \qquad \textbf{(16.4)}$$

Equation 16.4 is a linear equation in the form y = mx + b, and a plot of $\ln K_{eq}$ vs. $1/(R \cdot T)$ will yield a straight line with slope $-\Delta H^0$ and intercept S^0/R.

The equilibrium constant that governs the solution process is the **solubility product** K_{SP}. The chemical reaction for a solution equilibrium of an ionic salt M_nX_m is shown in equation 16.5:

$$M_nX_m(s) \underset{}{\overset{H_2O}{\rightleftharpoons}} n\ M^{p+}(aq) + m\ X^{q-}(aq) \tag{16.5}$$

The expression for the solubility product is given in equation 16.6:

$$K_{SP} = [M^{p+}(aq)]_{eq}^n \cdot [X^{q-}(aq)]_{eq}^m \tag{16.6}$$

The subscript *eq* indicates that the concentrations in equation 16.6 are *equilibrium concentrations*. The solution equilibrium is a *dynamic* chemical equilibrium, and a saturated solution has the same rate of precipitation and of dissolution. This dynamic equilibrium is schematically illustrated in Figure 16-3.

Figure 16-3: Dynamic chemical equilibrium of solution.

A caveat is in order when talking about solubility products and equilibrium constants. The solubility product as defined in equation 16.6 is a *stoichiometric equilibrium constant* or *concentration equilibrium constant*, whereas the equilibrium constant introduced in equation 16.3 is a *thermodynamic equilibrium constant*. In order to rewrite equation 16.6 as a thermodynamic equation, one has to replace *concentration c* by **activity** *a*, a dimensionless quantity. Activity *a* is related to concentration by means of the **activity coefficient** γ (equation 16.7)

$$a = \gamma \cdot c \tag{16.7}$$

In general terms, the activity coefficient is a measure of how a specific real system deviates from some reference system that is taken to be ideal. More specifically, the activity coefficient of a species is a measure of the effectiveness with which that species influences an equilibrium in which it is a participant. In very dilute solutions, the activity coefficient becomes unity and concentration and activity take on the same numerical value. However, with increasing concentration, an ion becomes more shielded by other surrounding ions, and loses some of its effectiveness. Therefore, the activity coefficient decreases with increasing concentration.

We can rewrite the solubility product K_{SP} as formulated in equation 16.6 as thermodynamical equilibrium constant, equation 16.8:

$$K_{eq} = a_{M^{p+}}^n \cdot a_{X^{q-}}^m = \gamma_{M^{p+}}^n [M^{p+}]^n \cdot \gamma_{X^{q-}}^m [X^{q-}]^m \qquad \textbf{(16.8)}$$

The individual ion activity coefficients are often replaced by a *mean ion activity coefficient* $\gamma\pm$ (equation 16.9).

$$\gamma_\pm^{n+m} = \gamma_{M^{p+}}^n \cdot \gamma_{X^{q-}}^m \qquad \textbf{(16.9)}$$

The following expression for the equilibrium constant governing a solution process is obtained from equations 16.6, 16.8 and 16.9:

$$K_{eq} = \gamma_\pm^{n+m} \cdot K_{SP} \qquad \textbf{(16.10)}$$

The concentration equilibrium constant K_{sp} provides a reasonable first approximation for the thermodynamic equilibrium constant K_{eq}, but needs to be corrected for activity in situations where the conditions are far from ideal, such as high concentrations.

As mentioned above, the solubility of many salts increases with increasing temperature. The solubility of salts is usually given as g(compound)/100g(solvent). A plot of mass of solute that can be dissolved in 100g of solvent vs. temperature is referred to as **solubility curve**. Solubility curves for selected inorganic salts are given in Figure 16-4.

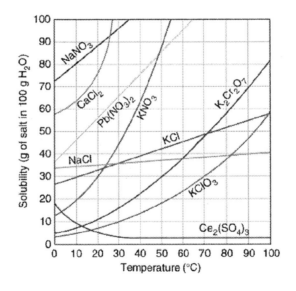

Figure 16-4: Solubility curves for inorganic salts.

When a system, in which solid salt and aqueous solution of that salt coexist, is first brought to an elevated temperature at which all the solid present dissolves, and then slowly cooled down, the onset of crystallization indicates a situation in which the dynamic chemical equilibrium between solid and solution is established. At the temperature at which the formation of crystals is first observed, the concentrations of cations and anions in solution are the equilibrium concentrations, from which the solubility product and the equilibrium constant can be calculated. In this experiment, we will use this concept in order to determine the solubility product of an inorganic salt at different temperatures.

16.3 Procedure

Temperatures will be measured with the accumet® AB15 pH/mV/°C Meter. From a piece of wire, construct a mixing element that you will use to stir the solution during its cooling process.

16.3.1 Preparation of salt solutions

Gather six medium test tubes and place them in a test tube rack. Place the first test tube into a 100 ml beaker and onto a balance, and tare the balance. Weigh out about 3 grams of potassium nitrate, KNO_3, into the first test tube, and record the mass to the nearest 0.01g. Repeat this step with the other five test tubes, weighing out approximately 4, 5, 6, 7, and 8 grams of KNO_3. Again, in your lab notebook record the masses to the nearest 0.01g. Clearly label each test tube. For example, label the test-tubes as #3, #4, #5, #6, #7, and #8 with reference to the approximate weight of potassium nitrate. Using a 10 ml graduated cylinder, add precisely 10ml of de-ionized water to each test tube. At this point, *do not stir* the contents of the test tubes.

16.3.2 Temperature-dependent solubility

Prepare a hot-water bath, adding approximately 300 ml of water to a 600-ml beaker. Use a Bunsen burner to bring the water to boil, then remove the Bunsen burner. Use a thermometer, and make sure that the temperature of the hot water bath stays above 65°C. During the experiment, it might be necessary to reheat the water bath with the Bunsen burner. Also prepare two cooling baths, one at a temperature of about 20°C, the other at a temperature of about 10°C. Use ice and warm tap water to achieve the required temperatures. Check the temperatures of the cooling baths occasionally.

Place the six test tubes as prepared in section 16.3.1 into the hot water bath. While the test tubes are warming up and equilibrating, all the salt contained in each test-tube should completely dissolve. Shake the test-tubes, or stir the solutions lightly to help the solid dissolve. After the solid in each test tube has completely dissolved in the water, remove all the test tubes from the hot water bath and place them in a test-tube rack. Add a few grains of "Ottawa Sand" to each test-tube to prevent formation of a supersaturated solution.

Insert the temperature probe into test-tube #8 and monitor the temperature reading. It is important to make sure that the water temperature is constant throughout the solution. Gently stir the solution during the cooling process.

Once crystallization begins, record the temperature, and move the temperature probe from test-tube #8 to test-tube #7. The onset of crystallization becomes apparent when a fluffy, white crystalline material appears and does not re-dissolve when the solution is stirred.

Repeat the above described procedure until crystallization has occurred in each of the test tubes. To help the cooling process, place test-tube #6 into the 20°C cooling bath after the temperature probe has been inserted. Do the same for test-tube #5. Place test-tube #4 into the 10°C cooling after the temperature probe has been inserted, and do the same for test-tube #3.

Reheat the test-tubes, and run the cooling experiment a second time. You should be able to reproduce the crystallization temperatures within 2°C.

16.4 Calculations

16.4.1 Experimental values for ΔH_{sol} and ΔS_{sol}

For each of the six solutions, calculate a value for K_{SP} at given temperature. Formulate the chemical reaction for the dissolution of potassium nitrate in water, and use this equation together with the mass of potassium nitrate used to prepare the solutions to calculate the concentrations of the ions in solution, and the solubility product.

Take the values for K_{SP} as an approximation for K_{eq}, and from the data collected in the six different measurements construct a plot of $\ln K_{eq}$ vs. $1/RT$. (Compare equation 16.4; make sure to convert temperatures from °C to K). Include the corresponding graph as part of your laboratory report, and report the equation of the line and R^2 values.

From the intercept and slope of the straight line derive values for ΔH_{sol}^{exp} and ΔS_{sol}^{exp}.

16.4.2 Accepted values for ΔH_{sol} and ΔS_{sol}

Use the following literature data to calculate accepted values for enthalpy and entropy of solution of potassium nitrate, ΔH_{sol}^0 and ΔS_{sol}^0.

	ΔH_f^0(kJ/mol)	S^0(J/mol·K)
KNO_3(s)	-494.6	133.1
K^+(aq)	-252.4	102.5
NO_3^-(aq)	-205.0	146.4

16.4.3 Mean ion activity coefficient $\gamma_\pm$

Use the following equation to derive an average value for the mean ion activity coefficient $\gamma_\pm$ of a potassium nitrate solution with a concentration in the range of the concentrations employed in this experiment:

$$\Delta S_{sol}^{exp} = \Delta S_{sol}^0 - R \cdot \ln \gamma_\pm^{m+n}$$

(16.11

16.5 Discussion

In your discussion, comment on possible systematic and random errors. Judge the accuracy of your experiment in comparison with the data obtained from literature values. Is the assumption of an ideal solution a valid one? Discuss your finding.

EXPERIMENT 17: Electrochemistry — Electrochemical Cells

17.1 Purpose

In experiment 17, we will construct different electrochemical cells. The formation constant of a complex ion will be determined by way of voltage measurements of electrochemical cells.

17.2 Background

The quintessential chemical reaction dealing with transfer of electrons is the **oxidation-reduction reaction** or **redox reaction**. Because electrons are transferred from one reactant to another, an oxidation-reduction reaction is capable of producing an electrical current. The device used to draw a current from an oxidation-reduction reaction is known as an **electrochemical cell**. The measure of how strongly the electrons are driven through the wire is given by the **voltage**, which is the energy per unit charge, and the voltage depends on both the *concentrations* and the *identities* of the species that make up the electrochemical cell. The voltage measured for an electrochemical cell is a measure for the driving force of the reaction itself, and therefore is referred to as **electromotive force** EMF.

If the species involved in a redox reaction are in direct contact, the electrons are transferred directly from one species to the other. For example, the reaction shown in equation 17.1 occurs *spontaneously*. If a strip of zinc is placed in a solution of copper(II) cation $Cu^{2+}(aq)$, the strip of zinc will begin to dissolve as the zinc metal is converted to zinc cation in solution $Zn^{2+}(aq)$, and copper metal is deposited on the surface of the zinc strip.

$$Zn(s) + Cu^{2+}(aq) \rightarrow Zn^{2+}(aq) + Cu(s) \tag{17.1}$$

To obtain work from this spontaneous transfer of electrons, the zinc and copper species must be separated so the electrons can be used as they flow from one species being oxidized to the species being reduced. An electrochemical cell employing the redox reaction of equation 17.1 can be constructed by placing a strip of zinc metal in a solution of zinc cations $Zn^{2+}(aq)$, and, in a separate container, a strip of copper in a solution of copper(II) cations $Cu^{2+}(aq)$. These electrodes comprise, respectively, the components of the oxidation and reduction half reactions, and the separate $M/M^{n+}(aq)$ systems are referred to as **half-cells**. Connecting the zinc and copper strips by a wire provides a path for electrons to flow from the zinc half-cell to the copper half-cell. If a voltmeter, a light bulb, or motor was attached to this wire, the electron flow or *electrical current* could be made to do work.

To complete the circuit and allow electrons to flow, a *salt bridge* is added between the two half-cells. The salt bridge allows ions to move into or out of the copper and zinc solutions without allowing any of the solutions to mix. A zinc-copper electrochemical cell is schematically depicted in Figure 17-1.

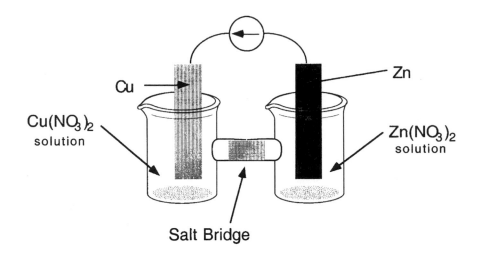

Figure 17-1: Electrochemical Cell

The salt bridge maintains electrical neutrality in the two solutions. As $Zn(s)$ is oxidized, the $Zn(s)$ is converted to $Zn^{2+}(aq)$, thus, the zinc ion concentration increases and the mass of the zinc metal decreases. Conversely, as $Cu^{2+}(aq)$, is reduced, the copper(II) cation is converted to solid copper; the mass of $Cu(s)$ increases at the expense of the concentration of $Cu^{2+}(aq)$ cation. Ions that are contained within the salt bridge are attracted towards the solution of increasing opposite charge. If for example a salt bridge is constructed from agar that is saturated with KNO_3 solution, nitrate anion $NO_3^-(aq)$ migrates towards the zinc half-cell to offset the increasing $Zn^{2+}(aq)$ concentration, and potassium cation the $K^+(aq)$ migrates towards the copper half-cell to offset the decrease in the $Cu^{2+}(aq)$ concentration.

Notice that, because $Zn(s)$ is being oxidized, the electrons flow from the Zn electrode to the Cu electrode. In keeping with conventional terminology for an electrochemical cell, the electrode where **oxidation** occurs is called the **anode** and the electrode where **reduction** occurs is called the **cathode**.

A **cell diagram** is an abbreviation for the pictorial representation of an electrochemical cell. A single vertical bar indicates a phase boundary. A double bar indicates the presence of a salt bridge. The components of the anode, the oxidation half reaction, are listed to the left of the double bar. The material on the extreme left is the anode. Occasionally, the electrode is not part of the reaction but an inert electrode. For example, platinum electrodes are often used when the oxidation of hydrogen is the anodic reaction. The components of the cathode, the reduction half reaction, are listed to the right of the double bar, and the material at the extreme right is the cathode. In this example, the cathode is both the product of the reduction reaction and the electrode. The *cell diagram* for the electrochemical cell shown in Figure 17-1 is given in equation 17.2.

$$Zn(s) \mid Zn(NO_3)_2(aq) \mid\mid Cu(NO_3)_2(aq) \mid Cu(s) \qquad \text{(17.2)}$$

The components on the left side of the double bar constitute the oxidation half-reaction, whereas the components on the right side of the double bar constitute the reduction half-reaction.

In order to compare cell voltages conveniently, a set of standard conditions is defined. Strictly speaking, standard state conditions are such that all gases must be at 1 bar pressure, approximately 1 atm, and all solutions must be of unit activity, approximately 1M concentration. All solutions, pure liquids and pure solids must be separated. The voltages for cells at standard conditions are called **standard cell potentials** and are symbolized by E^0_{cell}. Also, rather than tabulating standard voltages for all possible combinations of electrodes, the standard potentials for individual half reactions are tabulated. By convention, the half reactions are written as reduction half reactions and their standard voltages are called **standard electrode potentials** or **standard reduction potentials**, symbolized by E^0.

Since we cannot measure the potential of a single electrode but only the voltage or potential difference between two electrodes, standard cell potentials are measured for cells containing the desired electrode and a standard reference electrode. The reduction potential of the standard or reference electrode is arbitrarily set to 0.0 V. Thus, the measured cell potential is the reduction potential of the half reaction of interest. The **standard hydrogen electrode** (*SHE*) is the reference electrode that has been assigned a 0.0 V potential. The equilibrium reaction and the corresponding half-cell diagram are given in equation 17.3.

$$2H^+(a=1) + 2e^- \xrightleftharpoons{\text{on Pt}} H_2(g, 1bar) \ ; \ E^0 = 0V$$

$$Pt|H^+(a=1)|H_2(g, 1bar)$$

(17.3)

A negative E^0 indicates that H^+ is more easily reduced than the species of interest, whereas a positive $E°$ indicates that the species of interest is more easily reduced than H^+. For example, the iron(II) cation / iron half cell has a reduction potential of $E^0_{Fe^{2+}/Fe} = -0.44\,V$ .. The negative potential for this half reaction means that H^+ is more easily reduced than Fe^{2+}. In other words, given a choice between Fe^{2+} and H^+, electrons will go to H^+. One implication of this fact is that iron reacts with hydrochloric acid and forms molecular hydrogen.

Standard cell potentials for redox reactions — E^0_{cell} values — can be determined from standard electrode potentials for half-cell reactions — E^0 values. Keep in mind that the standard electrode potentials for half cell reactions are standard reduction potentials.

$$E^0_{cell} = E^0(reduction\ half-cell) - E^0(oxidation\ half-cell)$$

$$= E^0(cathode) - E^0(anode)$$

(17.4)

If E^0_{cell} cell is a positive number, then the reaction occurs spontaneously in the direction that it is written; the cell is a **galvanic cell**. If a reaction as written gives a negative value for E^0_{cell}, the reaction is not spontaneous. Instead, the reverse reaction will occur spontaneously.

In many practical instances, cell voltages are needed for non-standard conditions. A proper correction of the standard reduction potential takes into account deviations in activity as well as in stoichiometry.

Consider the following hypothetical reaction occurring in an electrochemical cell (equation 17.5):

$$a\ A + b\ B \rightarrow c\ C + d\ D \tag{17.5}$$

The reaction quotient Q for this reaction is given in equation 17.6:

$$Q = \frac{[C]_0^c \cdot [D]_0^d}{[A]_0^a \cdot [B]_0^b} \tag{17.6}$$

In equation 17.6, the subscripts refer to initial, not equilibrium concentrations, of the four species. If equilibrium concentrations were used, the expression of equation 17.6 would be the equilibrium constant K.

We also have to keep in mind that strictly spoken the equilibrium constants are *thermodynamic* equilibrium constant K_{eq}. K_{eq} is defined in terms of activities a, and equation 17.6 reads

$$Q = \frac{a_0^c \cdot a_0^d}{a_0^a \cdot a_0^b} \tag{17.7}$$

Activities are dimensionless numbers, and the activity of pure solids and pure liquids is 1. For dilute solution, the numerical value of the activity is approximately equal to the numerical value of the concentration of the dilute solution, $a \approx c$.

The **Nernst equation** relates the *actual cell voltage Ecell* to the reaction quotient Q (equation 17.8).

$$\tag{17.8}$$

$$E_{cell} = E_{cell}^0 - \frac{R \cdot T}{n \cdot F} \ln Q$$

Here, T is the temperature in K, n is the number of electrons transferred from the species being oxidized to the one being reduced, R is the gas constant, and F is Faraday's constant, 96485 Coulomb·mol-1.

The Nernst equation is often given in a simplified form by evaluating the constants given in the equation, assuming a temperature of 298.15 K, and converting the natural logarithm ln to the decadic logarithm log (equation 17.9).

$$E_{cell} = E_{cell}^0 - \frac{0.059}{n} \log Q \tag{17.9}$$

17.3 Procedure

Voltage will be measured will be measured by means of a standard instrument, such as the M-830B Digital Multimeter.

17.3.1 Setting up standard half-cells

Measure about 25 ml of 1.0M $ZnSO_4$, about 25 ml of 1.0M $CuSO_4$, and about 25 ml of 1.0M $FeSO_4$ into separate clean, dry 50 ml beakers. Obtain a strip of metallic zinc, a strip of metallic copper, and a strip of metallic iron. Metals have the tendency to develop a thin layer of metal oxide on their surface that does not conduct electrons and thus passivates the metal. Therefore, sand the three metal strips to obtain a clean and activated surface (*sand only the metal strips and not the counter*; it might be best to simply hold the metal strip in one hand while sanding). Place the metal strips in their corresponding solutions.

17.3.2 Measuring standard potentials

Construct and measure the standard potential for a zinc/copper, an iron copper, and a zinc/iron standard electrochemical cell. To construct a standard electrochemical cell, choose two half cells, and connect the half cells by a salt bridge. A piece of filter paper saturated with potassium sulfate solution acts as salt bridge. Do not allow the filter paper to become dry at any point during the experiment. Place the soaked paper across the two beakers of the half cells until each end is in contact with the solutions in the beakers.

When measuring the zinc/copper standard potential, connect the zinc strip to the black anode alligator clip, and connect the copper strip to the red cathode alligator clip. Record the voltage.

When measuring the iron/copper standard potential, connect the iron strip to the black anode alligator clip, and connect the copper strip to the red cathode alligator clip. Record the voltage.

When measuring the zinc/iron standard potential, connect the zinc strip to the black anode alligator clip, and connect the iron strip to the red cathode alligator clip. Record the voltage.

If the voltage for any of the standard electrochemical should read zero, either the alligator clips are not properly connected, or the salt bridge does not establish contact between the two half cells. Check and modify your experimental set-up until you receive a positive voltage output reading.

17.3.3 Measuring non standard potentials

For the zinc/copper system, set up a series of non standard electrochemical cells. Use the following pairs of zinc sulfate/copper sulfate concentrations to construct four non-standard electrochemical cells:

  i)   1.0M $ZnSO_4$ and 0.050M $CuSO_4$

  ii) 1.0M $ZnSO_4$ and 1.0 mM $CuSO_4$

  iii) 1.0 mM $ZnSO_4$ and 1.0 M $CuSO_4$

  iv) 1.0 mM $ZnSO_4$ and 1.0 mM $CuSO_4$

To set up electrochemical cells and half-cells, follow the procedure outlined in section 17.3.2, and obtain proper voltage readings.

17.3.4 The formation constant of [Cu(NH$_3$)$_4$]$^{2+}$

Caution: This experiment must be carried out in a fume hood!

Using a 10 ml graduated cylinder, add 5ml of 0.05M $CuSO_4$ solution to a 50ml clean and dry beaker, and dilute the solution by adding 20ml de-ionized water. Add 5ml of 1.50M NH_3 to the solution. The solution will turn dark blue, indicating the formation of the copper(II)-tetramine complex. Gently swirl the solution. Add a strip of copper metal to the solution and measure the cell potential against the $Zn(s)|Zn^{2+}(1.0M)$ half cell.

At the end of the experiment, dispose of the solutions in the appropriate waste containers.

17.4 Calculations

Table 17-1 lists relevant standard reduction potentials.

Table 17-1 Standard electrode (reduction) potentials at 25 ˚C.

Reduction half-reaction	E^0, V
$Cu^{2+}(aq) + 2e^- \rightarrow Cu(s)$	+0.340
$Fe^{2+}(aq) + 2e^- \rightarrow Fe(s)$	-0.440
$Zn^{2+}(aq) + 2e^- \rightarrow Zn(s)$	-0.763

Determine the potential for the Zn^{2+}/Zn half reaction $E^0_{Zn/Zn^{2+}}$ and for the Fe^{2+}/Fe half reaction $E^0_{Fe/Fe^{2+}}$, using the tabulated value for the Cu^{2+}/Cu half reaction $E^0_{Cu/Cu^{2+}}$ as standard. Use your values to predict the cell voltage for the $Zn(s) | ZnSO_4(aq) || FeSO_4(aq) | Fe(s)$ cell and compare with the measured value.

For each of the concentration cells set up in section 17.3.3, calculate the theoretical value of the cell potential using the Nernst equation.

From the experimental data in section 17.3.4, calculate the formation constant of the copper(II)-tetramine complex $[Cu(NH_3)_4]^{2+}$. To do so, first derive an expression for the formation constant Kf based on the following equilibrium reaction:

$$Cu^{2+} + 4\ NH_3 \rightleftharpoons \{Cu(NH_3)_4\}^{2+}$$

The complex formation constant K_f for the above equilibrium writes as

$$K_f = \frac{[\{Cu(NH_3)_4\}^{2+}]_{eq}}{[Cu^{2+}]_{eq} \cdot [NH_3]^4_{eq}}$$

From the measured cell-potential, one can now determine the concentration of Cu^{2+}-ions in solution. The spontaneous reaction in the corresponding electrochemical cell is

$$Zn(s) + Cu^{2+}(aq) \rightarrow Zn^{2+}(aq) + Cu(s)$$

and the corresponding Nernst-Equation writes as

$$E_{cell} = E^0_{cell} - (0.059/n) \cdot \log([Zn^{2+}]/[Cu^{2+}])$$

For E^0_{cell}, we obtain the following value (compare Table 17-1):

$$E^0_{cell} = E^0 (reduction) - E^0(oxidation)$$

$$E^0_{cell} = 0.340V - (-0.763V) = 1.103V$$

The cell is set up such that $[Zn^{2+}] = 1.0M$, and two electrons are involved in the cell reaction. Next, we solve for $[Cu^{2+}]$, which is equal to the concentration at equilibrium of the complex formation reaction:

$$\log[Cu^{2+}] = (2/0.059)\cdot(E_{cell} - E^0_{cell}) = (2/0.059)\cdot\Delta E$$

$$[Cu^{2+}] = 10^{33.9\cdot\Delta E}$$

We can derive expressions for the concentrations of all relevant species at equilibrium, using an ICE table. Since the equilibrium of complex formation lies far on the product side, we assume that the formation of the complex first goes to completion, and then establishes equilibrium.

	$[Cu^{2+}]$	$[NH_3]$	$[\{Cu(NH_3)_4\}^{2+}]$
Iinitial	0	$[NH_3]_{init} - 4[Cu^{2+}]_{init}$	$[Cu^{2+}]_{init.}$
Change	+x	+4x	-x
Equlibrium	+x	$[NH_3]_{init} - 4([Cu^{2+}]_{init} -x)$	$[Cu^{2+}]_{init.} - x$

We further make the simplifying assumption that the change x is negligible small compared to the initial concentration of copper cation, and we arrive at the following equilibrium concentrations:

$$[Cu^{2+}]_{eq.} = x$$

$$[\{Cu(NH_3)_4\}^{2+}]_{eq.} = [Cu^{2+}]_{init.} - x \approx [Cu^{2+}]_{init.}$$

$$[NH_3]_{eq} = [NH_3]_{init} - 4([Cu^{2+}]_{init} -x) \approx [NH_3]_{init} - 4[Cu^{2+}]_{init}$$

From these concentrations, a value for K_f can be obtained.

17.5 Discussion

Discuss your results in comparison with literature data (consult your "General Chemistry" textbook). When calculating the formation constant of $[Cu(NH_3)_4]^{2+}$, use an ICE table and show how the relevant equilibrium concentrations are obtained.

It is claimed that electrochemistry experiments are very sensitive, when small concentrations are involved. Based on your results, comment on this statement. Suggest possible improvements in the experimental procedure.

EXPERIMENT 18: Oscillating Reactions

18.1 Purpose

In experiment 18, the oscillatory Briggs-Rauscher reaction is investigated in terms of different initial conditions and different organic substrates.

18.2 Background

Most reactions proceed smoothly, at varying rates, to a final state of equilibrium. Some, however, do not. They oscillate in time: the concentrations of reactant, product, or intermediate species fluctuate wildly, often leading to easily observable oscillations of these concentrations *in time*. Other reactions are known that produce oscillations *in space* — waves of reactants, products, or intermediates show up.

Such **oscillatory** reaction systems are of great interest. Many natural phenomena, from firefly flashes to the heartbeat of mammals, are oscillatory chemical systems, and spatial oscillations, for example tiger stripes or zebra stripes, are also familiar. While oscillating biological reactions are incompletely understood, there are a number of known oscillating reactions among simple inorganic or organic molecules.

Many **oscillating chemical reactions** are often clock reactions. We recall that a **chemical clock** is a complex mixture of reacting chemical compounds in which the concentration of one component shows an abrupt change accompanied by a visible color effect (compare experiment 13). The *Briggs-Rauscher* reaction is a prominent example of an oscillatory reaction, and its concentrations of products and reactants can be approximated in terms of damped oscillations.

A typical Briggs-Rauscher system consists of

i) an aqueous solution of hydrogen peroxide H_2O_2

ii) an aqueous solution of an iodate, such as potassium iodate KIO_3.

iii) a strong, chemically unreactive acid, such as sulfuric acid H_2SO_4.

iv) divalent manganese cations Mn^{2+} as catalyst, which can be added as manganese sulfate $MnSO_4$.

v) An organic compound with an active, *enolic* hydrogen atom attached to carbon, R-H. The organic compound R-H will slowly reduce free iodine I_2 to iodide I^-. Malonic acid $HOOC-CH_2-COOH$ is an excellent organic compound R-H. Another organic substrate that has been suggested is acetone $H_3C-CO-CH_3$.

Starch is optionally added as an indicator to show the abrupt increase in iodide ion concentration [I^-] in the form of a sudden change from the orange or amber color of free iodine I_2 to dark blue of the iodine-starch complex. The iodine-starch complex consists of an incorporation of triiodide I_3^- ion into the coils of a starch molecule, and requires therefore both iodine I_2 and iodide I^-.

The complete reaction mechanism of the *Briggs-Rauscher* reaction is complex. It consists of about 30 individual reaction steps. Here, we will outline a few basic steps related to the production and consumption of the iodine species molecular iodine I_2 and iodide anion I^-.

The complete reaction mechanism of the *Briggs-Rauscher* reaction is complex. It consists of about 30 individual reaction steps. Here, we will outline a few basic steps that are related to the production and consumption of the iodine species molecular iodine I_2 and iodide anion I^-.

The overall stoichiometry of the Briggs-Rauscher reaction is shown in equation 18.1:

$$IO_3^- + 2\ H_2O_2 + R\text{-}H + H^+ \rightarrow R\text{-}I + 2\ O_2 + 3\ H_2O \tag{18.1}$$

We note that the reaction produces an organic iodide R-I, and proceeds under the evolution of oxygen gas. When the reaction is initiated, one observes the vigorous development of gas bubbles.

The overall reaction 18.1 can be broken into two component reactions. The first reaction involves the reduction of iodate IO_3^- to hypoiodus acid HOI:

$$IO_3^- + 2\ H_2O_2 + H^+ \rightarrow HOI + 2\ O_2 + 2\ H_2O \tag{18.2}$$

This reaction can occur by a *radical process* when the I^- concentration is *low*, or by a *non-radical process* when the I^- concentration is *high*. Both processes reduce iodate to hypoiodous acid. The radical process forms hypoiodous acid at a much faster rate than the non-radical process.

The HOI product of the first component reaction is a reactant in the second component reaction:

$$HOI + H\text{-}R \rightarrow I\text{-}R + H_2O \tag{18.3}$$

This reaction also consists of two component reactions:

$$I^- + HOI + H^+ \rightarrow I_2 + H_2O \tag{18.4}$$

$$I_2 + H\text{-}R \rightarrow I\text{-}R + H^+ + I^- \tag{18.5}$$

Furthermore, the hypoiodous acid reacts with hydrogen peroxide, and produces the initial amounts of iodide I^- that are needed to start the reaction sequence of the second component reaction:

$$HOI + H_2O_2 \rightarrow I^- + H^+ + O_2 + H_2O \tag{18.6}$$

The amber color is a result of the production of the I_2 in reaction 18.4. The I_2 forms because of the rapid production of HOI during the radical process. When the radical process is occurring, HOI is created faster than it can be consumed. Some of the HOI is used while excess is reduced by hydrogen peroxide to form I^-, reaction 18.6. The additional I^- produced reacts with iodine I_2 in an equilibrium reaction to form triiodide anion I_3^-:

$$I^- + I_2 \rightleftharpoons I_3^- \tag{18.7}$$

The I_3^- anion in turn reacts with the starch indicator to create the starch-iodine complex. The reaction mixture thus turns deep blue. The increasing I⁻ concentration reaches a point at which the non-radical process of HOI production takes over. However, the non-radical process does not produce HOI nearly as fast as the radical process. As a consequence, HOI does no longer enter reaction 18.6, and iodide is only consumed in reaction 18.4, but no longer produced in reaction 18.6. As a consequence, the equilibrium 18.7 shifts to the product side, and triiodide I_3^- is therefore removed from the reaction system. Thus, the solution changes its color back to amber. Eventually the I⁻ concentration drops low enough for the radical process to restart, and the cycle repeats itself.

18.3 Procedure

Utmost care is required when handling the chemicals for the Briggs-Rauscher reaction! Wear safety glasses and preferably safety goggles, as well as protective gloves, and perform the experiment in the hood!

18.3.1 Preparing the reaction solutions

Three different solutions are needed for the Briggs-Rauscher reactions. The solutions are prepared in 250 mL beakers, and stirred with glass stirring rods.

Solution A: Add 8.6 g of potassium iodate KIO_3 to 200 mL of 0.1M H_2SO_4. Stir the solution until the potassium iodate is dissolved.

Solution B: Add 3.6 g malonic acid $CH_2(COOH)_2$ and 1.0 g manganese sulfate monohydrate ($MnSO_4\cdot H_2O$) to 200 mL distilled water. Stir until the malonic acid is completely dissolved.

Solution C: Prepare a mixture of 80 mL of 30% hydrogen peroxide (H_2O_2) and 120 mL of distilled water.

18.3.2 The malonic acid reaction

The general procedure for the oscillation reaction is given below:

Add the 40 mL of solution A, the prescribed amount of solution B, and 1 mL of starch solution to a 250 mL Erlenmeyer flask. Stir or swirl the solution to mix. Add 40 mL of Solution C. Continue stirring or swirling the solution. Observe the development of oxygen, and monitor color changes. Time the reaction using a stopwatch. Once the reaction is initiated and stabilized — a time period of about 3-5 oscillations — start the stopwatch. Record the time whenever the solution turns from colorless or amber to dark blue. Record about 4-8 turning times during the course of the reaction.

18.3.3 Oscillation Frequency

Set up a table in which you report oscillation frequencies:

Trial	Time of Color Change (s)					
	1.	2.	3.	4.	5.	6.
1.						
2.						
3.						
4.						
5.						

Perform five trials using the following initial concentrations: Trial 1: 60 mL of solution B; Trial 2: 50 mL of solution B; Trial 3: 40 mL of solution B; Trial 4: 30 mL of solution B; Trial 5: 20 mL of solution B.

18.4 Calculations

or each trial, determine the initial concentrations of malonic acid $HOOC$-CH_2-$COOH$, and calculate oscillation frequencies (s-1) based on the time difference between two color changes. Caculate an average oscillation frequency. Set up a table to report your results:

Trial	[M.A.]$_{initial}$ (mol/L)	Oscillation frequency (s^{-1})					
1.		1.	2.	3.	4.	5.	Ave.
2.							
3.							
4.							
5.							

Use a spreadsheet, and construct a plot of initial concentration of malonic acid vs. oscillation frequency.

18.5 Discussion

In your discussion, comment on how your observations support the proposed mechanism. Address the influence of the initial concentration on the oscillation frequency.

EXPERIMENT 19: Chemical Kinetics II — the Activation Energy of Bromination

19.1 Purpose

In experiment 19, the activation energy of bromination reactions is determined based on temperature-dependent reaction rates.

19.2. Background

In **chemical kinetics**, valuable information of a chemical reaction is derived from an analysis of the rate or the speed of a reaction. Consider the hypothetical reaction displayed in equation 19.1:

$$aA + bB + cC \rightarrow gG + hH \tag{19.1}$$

The rate of the reaction can be measured by monitoring the *appearance* of the products G and H as well as by monitoring the *disappearance* of the reactants A and B. The **rate of reaction** v_r is then defined as follows:

$$v_r = -\frac{1}{a}\frac{\Delta[A]}{\Delta t} = -\frac{1}{b}\frac{\Delta[B]}{\Delta t} = -\frac{1}{c}\frac{\Delta[C]}{\Delta t} = \frac{1}{g}\frac{\Delta[G]}{\Delta t} = \frac{1}{h}\frac{\Delta[H]}{\Delta t} \tag{19.2}$$

Equation 19.2 shows how the reaction rate is determined from changes in concentration over time. By taking *negative* values of rates of disappearance, *positive* values of rates of appearance, and by dividing all rates by appropriate stoichiometric coefficients from the balanced equation, we ensure that we obtain the same positive-valued quantity v_r independent of the species for which the concentration is traced over time. The reaction rates in equation 19.2 result in an average value for the time interval Δt, and are referred to as **average reaction rates**. If we want to describe the reaction rate not over a time interval Δt but at some precise point in the reaction, the delta quantities in equation 19.2 are replaced by differentials, and we get

$$v_r = -\frac{1}{a}\frac{d[A]}{dt} = -\frac{1}{b}\frac{d[B]}{dt} = -\frac{1}{c}\frac{d[C]}{dt} = \frac{1}{g}\frac{d[G]}{dt} = \frac{1}{h}\frac{d[H]}{dt} \tag{19.3}$$

The rate of a chemical reaction can also be expressed in terms of concentrations of reactants, and for the hypothetical reaction of equation 19.1, one obtains the following expression:

$$v_r = k \cdot [A]^m \cdot [B]^n \cdot [C]^p \tag{19.4}$$

Such an experimentally determined relation is called a **rate law**, or **rate equation**. The *kinetic exponents*, here m, n and p, are generally small, positive whole numbers, although in some cases they may be zero, or non-integer numbers. Note that the kinetic exponents are not related to the stoichiometric coefficients. The kinetic exponents define the *order* of a reaction. The reaction of equation 19.4 then is of order m in A, of order n in B, of order p in C, and the *overall* order of reaction is the sum of the kinetic exponents. The characteristic proportionality constant k is called the **rate constant** of the reaction. Each reaction has its own characteristic value of k.

Whereas the rate law or rate equation for a chemical reaction links the reaction rate with concentrations of reactants and constant parameters, the **integrated rate equation** links concentrations of reactants with time. Integrated rate equations are generally derived for unimolecular reaction scenarios, equation 19.5:

$$A \rightarrow products \tag{19.5}$$

For a zero order reaction, for example, we obtain the following rate law

$$v_r = \frac{d[A]}{dt} = k \cdot [A]^0 = k \tag{19.6}$$

which when integrated results in the *integrated zero-order rate law*:

$$[A]_t = -k \cdot t + [A]_0 \tag{19.7}$$

Similar integrated rate laws can be obtained for first order and second order unimolecular reactions as well.

The treatment of unimolecular reactions is often sufficient for a kinetic analysis, since kinetic experiments can be designed such that a reaction of interest is reduced to a *pseudo* unimolecular reaction. When we consider the rate law of order $m+n+p$ of equation 19.4, and if the concentrations of reactants B and C remain constant over a period of time (this is often the case when they are in great excess with respect to reactant A) their concentrations can be included in the rate constant, resulting in a *pseudo* rate constant k':

$$k' = k \cdot [B]^n \cdot [C]^p \tag{19.8}$$

For the reaction of equation 19.1, the $(m+n+p)^{th}$ order rate equation has been reduced to a pseudo m^{th} order rate equation:

$$-\frac{d[A]}{dt} = K' \cdot [A]^m \tag{19.9}$$

Reaction rates not only depend on concentrations, but also on temperature; reactions generally proceed faster at higher temperatures. The temperature dependence of reaction rates is captured in the rate constant k; for each temperature T, a chemical reaction has a unique value of k.

The temperature dependence of the rate constant k allows one to determine the **activation energy** E_a of a chemical reaction. The **activation energy** E_a is the minimum energy above the *average kinetic energy* that molecules must posses for a chemical reaction to occur. A schematic diagram of the energy profile for a chemical reaction is displayed in Figure 19-1:

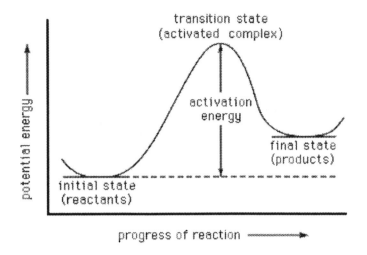

Figure 19-1: Schematic energy profile for the course of a chemical reaction.

Arrhenius was first to demonstrate that the rate constants k of many chemical reactions vary with temperature according to an exponential expression, equation 19.5, which is referred to as Arrhenius' equation:

$$k = A \cdot e^{-E_a/RT} \tag{19.10}$$

The proportionality factor A in equation 19.5 is known as *frequency factor*. It relates to the number of collisions per time that have the correct orientation to lead to products. Arrhenius' equation is often used in a form representing a straight line relationship, equation 19.11.

$$\ln k = -E_a \cdot \frac{1}{RT} + \ln A \tag{19.11}$$

19.2.1 Bromination of Acetone

The acid-catalyzed bromination of acetone, $CH_3C(O)CH_3$, is a classic example relating kinetics and reaction mechanism, and the landmark work by Lapworth published in 1904 provided much impetus for many researchers to employ kinetics when unraveling the complex mechanisms of chemical reactions. The corresponding equation for this reaction is displayed in equation 19.12:

$$CH_3C(O)CH_3 + Br_2 \xrightarrow{H+} CH_3C(O)CH_2Br + HBr \tag{19.12}$$

The reaction has been carefully studied; it turns out that it is first order in acetone and acid concentration, but is of order zero in bromine. Whenever the kinetic exponents are other than small, positive whole numbers, this usually indicates that the corresponding reaction mechanism consists of various elementary processes, each having their own reaction rate and contributing differently to the rate of the overall reaction. The form of the corresponding rate law is shown in equation 19.13:

$$v_r = k \cdot [Br_2]^0 \cdot [CH_3C(O)CH_3]^1 \cdot [H^+]^1 \tag{19.13}$$

The progress of a reaction over time can be measured by monitoring the concentration of one of the reactants or products. Since all products and all reactants but bromine are colorless, the kinetics of the bromination reaction is easily measured by monitoring the bromine concentration by means of absorption spectrophotometry (compare experiment 10).

By arranging the experimental conditions such that the concentration of one species is much smaller than the others, a technique known as *flooding,* the bromination reaction can be converted into a *pseudo* unimolecular reaction. If we choose the reaction conditions such that the concentrations of acetone and acid catalyst are large compared to the concentration of bromine and can therefore be considered as constant, the bromination of acetone turns into a pseudo-zero-order reaction, and the rate law reads as follows:

$$-\frac{d[Br_2]}{dt} = k'; \; k' = k \cdot [CH_3C(O)CH_3] \cdot [H^+]$$

(19.14)

From the integrated zero-order rate law, equation 19.7, we obtain the following expression for the *pseudo* rate constant *k'*:

$$k' = -\frac{[Br_2]_{t_2} \; [Br_2]_{t_1}}{t_2 - t_1} = -\frac{\Delta[Br_2]}{\Delta t}$$

(19.15)

19.2.2 Measuring Bromine Concentrations

We will trace changes in bromine concentrations by monitoring changes in absorption strength of the reaction mixtures. In the visible absorption spectrum of bromine, two strong absorption bands are found at wavelengths of 400nm and 450nm. The concentration of bromine will thus be monitored by measuring the absorption A_{400nm} of a reaction mixture over time at a wavelength of 400nm. According to Beer's law, the measured absorption A_{400nm} is directly proportional to the bromine concentration [Br2], equation 19.16 (compare experiment 10).

$$A_{400nm} = \varepsilon_{400nm} \cdot l \cdot [Br_2]$$

(19.16)

(In the following, we omit the subscript *400nm*; it is understood that all absorption measurements refer to a wavelength of 400nm.) Changes in bromine concentration $\Delta[Br_2]$ can therefore be calculated from changes in absorption, ΔA:

$$\Delta[Br_2] = -\frac{1}{\varepsilon \cdot l} \Delta A$$

(19.17)

From equations 19.15 and 19.17, it follows that *pseudo* rate constants can also be measured by monitoring changes in absorption over time:

$$k'' = -\frac{\Delta A}{\Delta t} \; ; k'' = \varepsilon \cdot l \cdot k'$$

(19.18)

Although abbreviated with the same symbol *A*, absorbance and frequency factor are not related to each other. However, from the context and the related formulas it usually becomes quite clear, whether *A* refers to absorbance or to the frequency factor.

19.2.3 Bromination of Ketones

The bromination reaction described for acetones also takes place for other ketones that have an H-atom in α-position to the carbonyl functionality. Key to the reaction mechanism is a keto-enol-tautomery that furnishes an intermediate with a C-C double bond:

$$\tag{19.19}$$

Thus, a ketone such as 2-butanone, $CH_3CH_2C(O)CH_3$, (commonly referred to as methyl ethyl ketone or MEK) can also undergo a bromination reaction (equation 19.20):

$$CH_3CH_2C(O)CH_3 + Br_2 \xrightarrow{H+} CH_3CH_2C(O)CH_2Br + HBr \tag{19.20}$$

The question then arises how the modification of the reactant will influence the reaction profile and in particular the activation energy of bromination of ketones. In experiment 19, we will determine the activation energy for the bromination of acetone and of 2-butanone and answer the question whether the presence of a methyl group in α-position to the carbonyl functionality will speed up or slow down the bromination reaction.

19.3 Procedure

Handling of the bromine stock solution and the preparation of reaction mixtures *must be carried out in a fume hood!* Chemical waste is to be collected in the waste beakers placed in the hoods.

The reaction product 1-bromopropan-2-one is a potential lachrymator. Poor laboratory technique will be most obvious, and will have your lab instructor in tears! However, in aqueous solution 1-bromopropan-2-one quickly decomposes by means of hydrolysis reaction, and is converted into environmentally benign decomposition products.

The reactants will be introduced by way of burets; make sure that you accurately measure out of proper amount of reactants. The following stock solutions will be used in the experiment:

1) 0.002M aqueous solution of bromine (Br_2)

2) 1.00M aqueous solution of hydrochloric acid (HCl)

3) 2.00M aqueous solution of acetone ($CH_3C(O)CH_3$)

4) 2.00M aqueous solution of 2-butanone ($CH_3CH_2C(O)CH_3$)

We will use a simple stop watch as timer for the bromination reaction.

19.3.1 Calibration of the Instrument

Absorptions are measured with a single-beam spectrophotometer, and the following instructions refer to the S42669PKND Fisher Educational Spectrophotometer. The general principles outlined apply to other spectrophotometers, such as the SPEC20, as well.

1. Turn on the spectrophotometer. Allow the instrument to warm up for at least 15 minutes in order to stabilize the lamp and detector.

2. Push the %T/A selector to choose the A (Absorbance) operating mode.

3. Turn the wavelength control knob to 400nm.

4. Move the second order filter lever position to the appropriate filter setting. For measurements at 400nm, push in the second order filter lever until the blue dot is showing.

5. Absorptions of reaction solutions will be measured using a tubular test tube cuvette. Fill a cuvette with blanking solution. Here, we use de-ionized water as blanking solution. The cuvette should be at least 2/3 full. Place the test tube cuvette into the sample compartment. Be sure that the test tube cuvette has been firmly pressed into the sample compartment and the lid of the sample compartment has been closed.

6. Adjust the display to 0.00A by turning the 100%T/A control.

7. Remove the cuvette from the sample compartment.

19.3.2 Set up of water baths at different temperatures

The bromination reactions will be carried out at four different temperatures. Room temperature (r.t.) refers to a temperature of $25\pm5°C$. Warm (w.) refers to a temperature of $35\pm5\ °C$. Luke-cold (l.c.) refers to a temperature of $15\pm5\ °C$, and cold (c.) to a temperature of $10\pm5\ °C$.

Fill four 250 mL beakers with about 100 mL of water. Use a bunsenburner or a hot plate, as well as ice, and set-up r.t., w., l.c., and c. water baths. Frequently monitor the temperature of your water baths. If the temperature falls out of the w., l.c. or c. range, re-heat the water bath, or replace some water with additional ice.

19.3.3 Rates of Bromination

The basic procedure for measuring the *pseudo* rate constants k" for the bromination reaction consists of the following steps:

1. Charge three 18×150mm test tubes with 1 mL of ketone solution, 1 mL of hydrochloric acid solution and 3 mL of bromine solution, respectively. The ketone solution is either the acetone solution, or the 2-butanone solution. Place the test-tubes and a tubular test tube cuvette into a water bath of desired temperature. Keep the test tubes for a few minutes in the water bath before initiating the reaction. This way, you will raise or lower the temperature of the reactants, and equilibrate the reactants as well as the cuvette to the temperature of the water bath.

2. Add the 1 mL of ketone solution, the 1 mL of hydrochloric acid solution and the 3 mL of bromine solution into the tubular test tube cuvette. Make sure that you gently swirl the test tube cuvette in order to mix their contents and to produce a homogeneous solution. Place the cuvette into the water bath for additional one or two minutes.

3. Measure the temperature of the water bath, and record the temperature in your notebook. Place the test tube cuvette into the sample compartment of the spectrophotometer. Be sure the test tube cuvette has been firmly pressed into the sample compartment and the lid of the sample compartment has been closed. Monitor the absorption at a wavelength of 400nm. When you observe a drop of 0.01 units in the absorbance reading, start the timer. Continue monitoring the absorbance reading. Whenever the absorbance drops by an additional 0.01 units, record the time in your lab notebook. You should record at least three time intervals, and each corresponding to a drop in absorbance of 0.01 units. Since the reaction is of zero order with respect to bromine, the time intervals – ideally being identical - should be close to each other within a few seconds. Significant changes in time intervals are often due to changes in temperature.

4. An alternative procedure is based on measuring the absorption at fixed time intervals, for example every ten or twenty seconds. However, this procedure takes considerably longer time, and it is more likely that the temperature will significantly change during the time period when the data are collected. Compare the calculation section 19.4 for a set of sample data that illustrates reasonable absorption values and time intervals.

19.3.4 Bromination of Acetone and 2-Butanone

Measure the rates of bromination for acetone at four different temperatures that fall into the r.t.-, w.-, l.c.- and c.-range. For each of the measurements, follow the procedure as outlined in section 19.3.3.

Measure the rates of bromination for 2-butanone at four different temperatures that fall into the r.t., w., l.c. and c. range. Follow the procedure as outlined for the rate of bromination of acetone.

Throughout the experiment, work efficiently and in a speedy manner. You want to avoid any effects due to a change in temperature, once the reaction mixture is removed from the warm or from the cold water bath.

In your lab notebook, set up tables for acetone kinetics, as well as for 2-butanone kinetics, in which you record your results:

Ketone

r.t.: T =		w.: T =		l.c.: T =		c.: T =	
t	A	t	A	t	A	T	A
0 s		0 s		0 s		0 s	

19.4 Calculations

Activation energies for bromination reactions are calculated based on the temperature dependence of the rate constant k (compare equations 19.10 and 19.11). From the data collected, which refer to change in absorption over time, we can calculate a pseudo rate constant k" = $\Delta A/\Delta t$ (compare equation 19.18). The true rate constant k is directly related to the pseudo rate constant $k"$:

$$k" = \varepsilon \cdot l \cdot k' \Rightarrow k' = k"/\varepsilon \cdot l$$
$$k' = k \cdot [CH_3C(O)CH_3] \cdot [H^+] \Rightarrow k = k'/([CH_3C(O)CH_3] \cdot [H^+])$$
$$\Big\} k = k"/(\varepsilon \cdot l \cdot [CH_3C(O)CH_3] \cdot [H^+])$$

The above derivation is based on equations 19.18 and 19.14. We can substitute the expression for k in Arrhenius' equation 19.10:

$$k"/(\varepsilon \cdot l \cdot [RCH_2C(O)CH_3] \cdot [H^+]) = A \cdot e^{-E_a/RT}$$
$$\Rightarrow k" = \varepsilon \cdot l \cdot [RCH_2C(O)CH_3] \cdot [H^+] \cdot A \cdot e^{-E_a/RT}$$
$$\Rightarrow k" = F \cdot e^{-E_a/RT}; \ F = \varepsilon \cdot l \cdot [RCH_2C(O)CH_3] \cdot [H^+] \cdot A$$

Since the frequency factor A, the absorptivity coefficient ε, and the cell length l are all constants, and since the experiment was carried out such that the acid concentration $[H^+]$ and the ketone concentration $[RCH_2C(O)CH_3]$ remain to a first approximation constant, all these values can be combined into one proportionality factor F. Following equation 19.11, we get the following relationship:

$$\ln k" = -E_a \cdot \frac{1}{RT} + \ln F$$

Thus, a plot of ln $k"$ vs. 1/RT results in a straight line, the slope of straight line being equal to the activation energy E_a.

A set of sample data is given below:

Acetone kinetics

T: 20.0° C		T: 27.0° C		T: 13.5° C		T: 1.5° C	
t (s)	A	t (s)	A	t (s)	A	t (s)	A
0	0.17	0	0.15	0	0.70	0	0.22
20	0.12	10	0.11	15	0.65	30	0.20
40	0.08	25	0.06	45	0.57	50	0.18
50	0.06	38	0.02	110	0.54	73	0.16
60	0.04	45	0.00	300	0.52	120	0.14

Set up a table in your lab notebook in which you report $k"$ values. Recall that $k" = -\Delta A/\Delta t$. Convert the temperature from degree Celsius into degree Kelvin. Values for the acetone kinetics are given below:

	acetone			
	T= 293.2 K	**T= 300.2 K**	**T= 286.7 K**	**T= 274.5 K**
1st k" (2.-1.)	2.5E-03	4.0E-03	3.3E-03	6.7E-04
2nd k" (3.-2.)	2.0E-03	3.3E-03	2.7E-03	1.0E-03
3rd k" (4.-3.)	2.0E-03	3.1E-03	4.6E-04	8.7E-04
4th k" (5.-4.)	2.0E-03	2.9E-03	1.1E-04	4.3E-04
Average $\bar{k}$"	2.1E-03	3.3E-03	1.6E-03	7.4E-04

Use a spreadsheet such as Excel to create a straight-line plot of $\ln\bar{k}$"vs 1/RT. Enter the data of the table above into two columns of your spreadsheet. Then, convert the column of rate constant k" values into a column of ln k" values, and the column of temperature T values into a column of 1/RT values. Make sure that temperature values are converted into degree Kelvin K. Use the right value of the gas constant R (8.314 J/mol·K). Create a plot of ln k" vs 1/RT, and fit a trendline to the data points. The slope of the trendline yields the negative value of the activation energy of the bromination reaction (in J/mol). Include this plot as part of your lab report. A plot for the sample data is shown below:

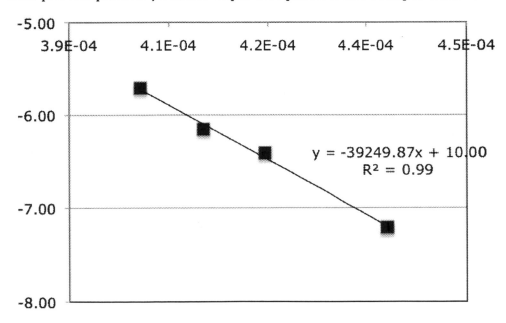

In your note book, summarize values of the activation energies for the bromination of acetone, and for the bromination of 2-butanone. Report the activation energies in units of kJ/mol. For the given example the activation energy amounts to 39 kJ/mol.

19.5 Discussion

Summarize the results that you obtained from this reaction. What activation energies did you find? If they are different between the two compounds, explain why you think that is so. Did raising or lowering the temperature affect the rate of the reaction? Did the different ketones being used cause a change in the activation energy? Explain how your results may have differed had you used: Less acetone, less hydrochloric acid, or less bromine.